BOOK OF THE
KINDRED

BY MARK REIN·HAGEN

GRAEME DAVIS

TOM DOWD

DON BASSINGTHWAITE

LAWRENCE WATT-EVANS

MATT FORBECK

JIM MOORE

Book of the Kindred
Written by: Mark Rein•Hagen with Graeme Davis, Tom Dowd and Don Bassingthwaite, Lawrence Watt-Evans, Matt Forbeck and Jim Moore
Developed by: Mark Rein•Hagen and Ken Cliffe
Edited by: Ken Cliffe, Erin Kelly and Stewart Wieck
Vice President in Charge of Production: Richard Thomas
Art by: Timothy Bradstreet and Joshua Gabriel Timbrook
Cover and interior design by: Michelle Prahler

White Wolf's World Wide Web Address:
http://www.white-wolf.com

CONTENTS

◆

FOREWORD

✦

MARK REIN·HAGEN

I'm the guy who made all this shit up.[i] All the stuff about blood, sex and the undead, and the dross like "the beast within" and "lest a beast I become." It was, and is, all for a Storytelling game called **Vampire: The Masquerade**. Sometimes I just don't understand what happened to my little game; how it got so out of hand and became, in its own weird way, something of a cultural phenomenon, whatever that is.[ii]

It has gone from a Storytelling game to a line of novels to a computer game to a television show — **Kindred: The Embraced**. People as famous as Francis Ford Coppolla have asked me to sign their books.[iii] (Cool, huh?) The clan concept is about to be stolen by every wanna-be west of the Rockies. Whether it's the Ventrue, Brujah or Toreador, the tale is always the same (with hand to forehead): "Life is unlivable, unlife is worse, but at least I'm a cool cat."

If there's one thing I've learned, it's that it is truly bizarre to listen to someone you don't know from Adam bandy about words and ideas that once belonged to you.[iv] The ideas that make up the World of

---

[i] Me in the plural. (i.e., With the help of many brilliant friends more talented than I. Creativity is hiding your sources.)

[ii] I could probably come up with some sort of definition for C.P., but I just hate people who don't express some minor degree of humility, no matter how fake.

[iii] It's true! It's just that he had no clue who I was... but someday he will!

[iv] And equally bizarre to hear them claim those ideas as their own, as if no one would know. Some people just don't know how to hide their sources, I guess.

Darkness and the culture of the Kindred were once idle dreams and fantasies — *my* idle dreams and fantasies — and now they have taken on a life of their own. People I don't even like talk to me about Kindred and Embraces, and some even call me up in the middle of the night and drone on about diablerie and the Sabbat.[v] People, for some reason, have paid attention, and to tell the truth it freaks me out.[vi]

I can't decide whether to be proud or horrified — part of me wishes these ideas still belonged solely to me, so I could fiddle with them more. I don't like to set anything in stone, and I don't like well-aged thoughts that no longer bend to my will. I hate that this world of the undead is now beyond my control and I can't do my will upon it. Others use it, live it and guide it, and there is little room for any of its creators anymore (we have the wrong instincts, you see).[vii] It now exists more in the dreams and fantasies of *others* than in my own. It no longer belongs to me, or really, anyone.[viii] If some little old lady in Topeka watches the show and gets more of a rise out of it than I do, who does it really belong to?

---

[v] Though sometimes it's an agent from CAA or Paradigm who wants to talk about setting you up with some Hollywood "cool cats." Yes, Yes, Yes! Do me, Walt!

[vi] That's not to say that telling the truth is my particular forte....

[vii] As in me. I only like the starts of things, when everything is raw and new; endings are always so bloody dull. (Or lets put it this way: Some people just don't have a talent for detail or dedication, but do have the gift of gab).

[viii] This heresy cannot go by without the reminder that, of course, all White Wolf copyrights and trademarks still stand.

So, you might ask, why am I writing this insipid Foreword?[ix] Well there are many reasons, but the only important one is that I enjoy preaching nearly as much as my father does,[x] and the editor told me to have 1500 words by tomorrow morning or else. So, you'll either have to bear with me or skip onto the real meat — the rest of the book, that is. You may or may not be familiar with this material, but remember, this is the original stuff.

Damn, it seems like yesterday (or perhaps another lifetime altogether) that the folks behind this material all lived together in a rotted-out, flea-infested house with 300 boxes of unsold books sitting on the front porch. We didn't have any money, but we had each other.... Well, we had a book to write and a company to run at least.

Oh, it was tragic. I had no car, no bike, no quarters for arcades and no beer. For nine months, everything in my life centered around the twisted little world that spun around in my head. My parents, though they won't admit it now, thought I was heading down the freaky highway of doom, but my grandparents, bless their souls, lent us the money to pay for the first print run of books.[xi] We were in business!

The first print run sold out in a few weeks, so we printed another one, and we kept doing it. Next thing we knew, we had built a real

---

[ix] Truth is, I own part of the company that printed this book. (White Wolf, that is. Note our fine collection of Storytelling games and classic and contemporary fiction, no doubt shamelessly advertised in the back of this book.)

[x] He's a Lutheran minister. Ironic, eh, me being a horror writer and all? Nudge, nudge; wink, wink.

[xi] Of course, my partner's parents always forked up some cash, too, but he can talk about that in his own damn Foreword.... When he finally gets one. Ha!

publishing company, probably the only one in the country owned by people under 50, much less run by a staff of people almost all under the age of 30. People liked our complex, convoluted world of clashing egos and passions, and its success led to even more books and the television show that you watch today.[xii] Whether it's wraiths or changelings, Moorcock or Ellison, we have a book for you. In a few short years, we've gone from Dunkin' Donuts to smoked salmon, from watching 90210 to meeting Tori herself in all her greatness.

So, that's the sordid tale of how all this folklore and mythology got slung together and how it made a bunch of money.[xiii] I'd go on; the story isn't done, but my word count is nearly up. So, whoever you are, please find something interesting in the following pages or none of it will have been worthwhile. Enjoy it if you can, despise it if you can't, but please, please, please — recycle.[xiv]

Pssssst. Remember none of this shit is true. We made it all up. Pass it along.

[xii] So (warm smile), why don't you check out the back of this book for descriptions of some of the other books that we have available.

[xiii] Boy, I'd love to see some of that dough — I could eat enough Chubby Hubby to choke a cow!

[xiv] A wasted mind is worse than a wasted life. Remember, your job is to process information and pass on what's good to the next person. If you like this book or anything in it — or any other book, for that matter — pass it along, Bozo! If you don't get the idea, read *The Lucifer Principle* (but ignore *The Turner Diaries*).

*T*he centuries stretch before you, beckoning. There is little in this world that is not within your reach or grasp. Now you are free, no longer a gear in a machine. The world is your stage, and all of its people mere props in your hands.

You are a predator, a hunter who feeds upon others to survive. Around you moves a great herd, blind to your presence, unaware of the threat you pose. Ignorant, they perform the quiet motions of their lives, each simple action and gesture increasing your attraction to them. They are beauty beyond words.

You do not crave money or clothing, riches or power, though you may desire such as a passing fancy. The only thing you truly need is blood — the river of life coursing through the veins of each and every human. That is the price for what you have become — and it may cost you your soul. Blood is the be all and end all of your existence. But what an existence it is!

Day has become night, and night has become day. In the night, you are all-powerful; no mortal can surpass your potency. Neither bullets nor blades can end your existence. Only the sun do you fear. Its accursed rays bring the kiss of death.

But that is not all, for neither are you alone. Others call this world their playground, and the playground is only large enough for so many. All Kindred are your brothers and sisters now, but even brother may kill brother, even as did the first of your kind.

Beyond the other Kindred there are the Lupines, the Magi, the Arcadian brethren, and some even say the Shades of the netherworld. Though not all

are opposed to you, they do not tolerate your presence in their realms. But, sometimes two fates become intertwined.

Above all other dangers stands the wash of humanity. You are but a parasite, and if your host knew of your existence, you would be crushed like a flea between pinching fingers. The slightest mistake can bring the Inquisition, with its burning torches, to the door of your haven. The Masquerade must go on, and none may learn of your existence — lest life-in-death become final death.

Though you face great peril, there is no doubt that you are a creature of immense strength. Your mystical powers are vast and your potential unparalleled. The only thing over which you do not have complete control is yourself. Your limitations lie not in what you can do, but in who and what you are. The Beast that lurks within you may rise up at any time, destroying all that you touch and dare to love. It is you, yourself, not the perils and enemies you face, who makes your life a nightmare.

And as your humanity slowly slips away, you may begin to realize just what it is you have lost.

CHAPTER ONE
SMOKE

✦

DON BASSINGTHWAITE

Anyone standing on the icy midnight street might have noticed that the man in the deep blue overcoat did not exhale. Brahms took a deep drag on his cigarette and leaned back against the doorway. The warm smoke curled through his grave-cold lungs and settled like a purring cat in his chest. Could vampires get cancer? Brahms didn't think so.

He let the smoke flow gently up from his lungs and out his mouth. The window beside him made a mirror, and he studied the effect carefully, allowing his face to assume the intense, bright-eyed look that had led his sire to Embrace a starving young composer. Brahms frowned and relaxed his features, then added the crowning touch to his Masquerade. Careful rhythmic bursts of smoke, long practiced, would pass for the condensation of breath in the winter air.

A door opened down the street. Brahms faded back into the shadows and waited for his quarry to pass. The homeless, the easiest prey at other times of the year, were packed into shelters or huddled together for warmth during the winter. Brahms had been forced to become more creative in his stalking. Solitary mortals could occasionally be found here, walking to the home of Grosse Madeleine, medium and fortuneteller, too ashamed to come during the day or in groups. However, Brahms' creativity proved dangerous. Madeleine may have only pretended to the powers of a mage, but she did have true knowledge of the Kindred. Madeleine was not to be trifled with.

But it was not the middle-aged woman whom Brahms watched

leaving the shop. It was a young man, woefully underdressed for the weather. He did not shiver in the swirling snow, though, and Brahms recognized the emblem painted on his torn denim jacket. A black-bladed knife. One of the Sabbat who had recently slipped into the city. Brahms bit his lip. The Sabbat were ungodly dangerous. But, the prince would probably like to know what the Sabbat were doing at Grosse Madeleine's house. He stepped out of the doorway and began to follow silently.

The Sabbat vampire went directly to an old factory by the river. Unlike Brahms, he did not attempt to stick to the shadows. He walked boldly through the streets and into the shell of the factory. Brahms, adopting greater stealth, carefully scanned the area for lookouts. None. The crumbling walls of the factory made easy climbing, and he was soon crouched on the ledge of a paneless window, looking down at a scene that might have inspired Dante.

Fires burning in oil drums cast a flickering light across the twisting, blood-slicked bodies of dancing vampires. Cruel, savage rock-and-roll lifted them and threw them down again. Brahms felt their frenzy touch him, and he shivered, fighting for control. At the center of the hellish dance stood an old vampire, his power covering him like a cloak. Around him were spread knives and smoking braziers, an obsidian mirror that must have been ancient, and a fine crystal goblet that might have held red wine... had the liquid in it not been thick, opaque and still steaming with life's heat. The elder stood silently, unmoved by the frenzy, watching as the youth with the torn jacket wove through the dancers. The young Sabbat's eyes darted about the room, and his lips wavered between a snarl and a cry. He held himself

erect, however, and walked to the elder on unsteady legs. Not a vampire, Brahms realized, but a mortal under the control of the Sabbat, probably a ghoul. "The eye of a seer," the ghoul said as he handed the elder a small package. Brahms heard the words clearly over the beating music.

Brahms knew little of the occult, but recognized sorcery when he saw it. The Sabbat elder knew the secrets of Thaumaturgy, somehow operating outside the laws that clan Tremere placed upon blood magic, and so was twice as dangerous for it. Knowing it would do him no good, Brahms crossed himself as the elder unwrapped the package and took out an object that looked for all the world like a child's marble.

The tide of the music receded as the elder began a droning chant in some long-dead language — the goblet of blood in one hand, the eye of Grosse Madeleine in the other. The young man knelt before him. In the whole cavernous corpse of the factory, only the dancing vampires, caught in their frenzy, and the leaping flames of the fires moved. The elder's chant rose to a crescendo, and, abruptly, he dropped the eye onto a brazier and dashed the blood over the obsidian mirror. While the eye sizzled on the hot coals, the elder gazed intently into the bloody mirror. At the same moment the eye collapsed into ashes, the Sabbat turned away, apparently satisfied with what he had seen. The young man still stood, facing him.

"You did well." The dancing vampires almost moaned in response to the elder's praise of the mortal. "Soon you will be ready to receive our Embrace."

"Soon?"

"Yes, soon. But you are now ready to receive the name you will bear as a vampire." Again the dancing vampires moaned, louder this time. A note of celebration. "We are predators. We feed upon the humans who were our brothers and sisters when we were alive. Do you understand this?"

"Yes."

This time, the dancing vampires moaned to the words of the mortal. The elder nodded. "You have come to accept what this will mean?"

"Yes."

"What is that?"

Quietly. "I must kill."

"What?"

"I must kill."

The dancing vampires roared their approval, but the elder waved for them to be silent.

"You seem reluctant."

The mortal swallowed. "I must kill!"

"Yes. There is no other way to survive. You must kill for the blood of humans." He paused and ran his fingers through the long, thick red hair of the mortal. "You are the first in a great many years to seek us out and request to be Embraced." He smiled cruelly. "You are a traitor to humankind. Your name as a vampire shall be Judas."

The roar of the dancers was deafening. The music, all but forgotten, returned at an intensity seemingly three times what it had been before. The very concrete and steel of the factory strained to respond to the savage call. The young man stood on the edge of the eye of the storm, torn between fury and calm. He glanced at the elder, who smiled again. Doubt, sorrow, and thought all forgotten with the frenzy, the mortal lifted his face and screamed wild ecstasy. He plunged into the dance, released. No vampire would harm him, no matter how much the Beast raged. He was Judas, their future kin.

Brahms stood silently and slipped back out the window. He had seen enough.

Two days later, he saw the red-haired mortal again.

He was in a store, trying on leather jackets. Brahms walked silently up behind him. "Judas," he whispered.

The young man started and swung around, panic clearly showing on his face. Fast for a mortal, but far slower than a Kindred. He wasn't even a ghoul. From the look in his eyes, Brahms knew Judas had recognized him almost immediately as a vampire. The boy was clever. He had assumed a sublime indifference and casually turned away from Brahms before anyone else in the store could have noticed his actions.

"I didn't recognize you without the knife." He pulled on the denim jacket he had worn before, nonchalantly checking his hair in the mirror.

Brahms almost smiled. "There are some of us you haven't seen yet."

"I guess so. Did Jeremiah send you?"

Ah, the Sabbat elder. "No." He slid an appreciative hand over one of the leather jackets Judas had been trying on. "Nice."

"I wanted something, you know… for after."

"Why wait for the Embrace?" Brahms ran the sleeve of the jacket under his nose, breathing in the dark, heavy smell of the leather. He glanced up at the young man. "Get one now."

"Can't afford it."

"Can't afford it?"

Judas reacted like an angry cat, almost visibly attempting to make himself look bigger and tougher — the Judas the Sabbat wanted to see. Brahms realized that maybe this wouldn't be so tough after all. He laughed, deflating Judas a little, then flashed him that mad-bright expression his sire had loved.

"They call me Brahms, Judas. Come hunt with me."

Judas deflated a little more, then struggled back with a snarl. "You know Jeremiah won't let me hunt until I've been Embraced." The elder was playing games with him. That would explain why he wasn't even a ghoul. Brahms had twisted rules even when he was alive. "To drink maybe," he snarled back, a snarl frightening enough to slam Judas back down, "but not to hunt." He pushed Judas toward the front of the store. "How can he expect you to run before you can crawl?"

Surprisingly, Judas could run. Really run. He kept up with the pace Brahms set, although it was clear he found it tiring. He was quiet, too. They slipped through the near darkness of the park's shadows, the moon throwing just enough light onto the snow so that Judas could run without stumbling. Brahms kept them to the paths. Why humiliate Judas by leading him into the underbrush? They continued through the still night, to the other side of the park where a few modest homes backed onto the woods. Brahms stopped abruptly and motioned Judas to do the same. The young man slowed, but kept moving, walking, stretching and breathing heavily.

Brahms glanced at him. "You a marathon runner?"

"Orienteering. High school medallist."

"You don't look like an athlete."

Judas dropped to a crouch beside him. "You don't look like a vampire." He ducked his head, took another deep breath, then looked up again. "I took it up. As a hobby." Pulling aside the branches of a bush, he looked out at the houses. "Which one?"

"There. That one." A pleasant house, neat and well kept.

The walk was shovelled clean of all but a dusting of new-fallen snow. Brahms knew the woman who lived there, a widow who habitually fell asleep while watching television. When he came to her while she slept, she thought he was her dead husband. He smiled at the memory. That was one reason his sire had named him Brahms — he preferred to feed only when his vessels were asleep. Judas didn't know that, of course. Motioning Judas to follow, Brahms crept around to the front of the house.

"I'm going to ring the bell. You," he whispered, positioning Judas around the corner of the building, "stay here. I'll be back. When she opens the door, you charge her. Shove her back into the house and hold her for me. Got it?" Brahms pulled back his lips to expose his fangs and ran his tongue along them. Judas swallowed and nodded. Silently, Brahms ran up the porch and pressed the doorbell twice. He caught the faint sounds of the woman stirring inside, sitting up, turning off the television, and walking toward the door. He vaulted the porch railing and rejoined Judas around the corner. "Ready?"

The door opened. "Hello? Hello?" Judas was holding his breath.

So, to his surprise, was Brahms. He nudged Judas to imply, "Now!"
The porch creaked as the woman stepped outside to look up and
down the street. "Hello?"

The moment was perfect. Brahms nudged Judas again. Judas shook
his head and refused to meet his gaze. Brahms gritted his teeth. Now
or never, Judas. He shoved him out into full sight. For a moment,
Judas just stood there, breath steaming red-gold in the warm light
that streamed from the open door. Brahms could almost see the
widow standing on the porch, her own mouth open in shock, and he
wondered who would react first.

It was Judas. He turned and fled, running down the street as fast as
he could. The widow screamed and slammed the door. Brahms could
hear her inside, dialing the phone, probably calling the police. He ran
after Judas. He caught him in a schoolyard. For the first time, Judas
was shivering in the cold.

"What the hell was that? Why didn't you take her?" Brahms spun
Judas around so they were face to face. Judas collapsed to his knees.
Tears were running down his face. "I couldn't! I can't! This isn't the
way it's supposed to be!"

Brahms crouched beside him and put his lips close to Judas' ear.
"How is it supposed to be, Judas? You want to be one of us, don't
you?"

"Not if it means this! Not if it means killing old women!"

"I thought you accepted that. Isn't that what you told Jeremiah? 'I
must kill'?"

"I lied!" He struggled to his feet and ripped open his jacket and
shirt, baring his chest and neck to the moonlight and cold, clear air.

"Go ahead! Kill me! That's the price for lying, isn't it? I know the price, kill me!"

All Brahms could do was stare at his chest. It was lean and lightly muscular, but his skin was marred by dozens of scars. Old scars, from wounds cut deliberately and with care. Brahms pulled the shirt and jacket out of the boy's hands, tugging them down to reveal his back — more scars, but lighter and less regular. The scars of a lash, but from an angle.

"You did this to yourself?" Softly. He didn't have the heart to torment the young man any longer.

Judas nodded and a sob escaped his throat. "Everything is too damned ordinary!" He pulled away from Brahms and let his shirt and jacket fall completely to the ground. "The world is dead! I need to know there's something more than just.... I know there's more out there, I can feel it. I need to feel."

"So pain is the answer?"

"No. It wasn't, not in the end. It worked for a while — I felt something, but...." He grasped at the air and then closed his fists. "Then it just hurt, and I felt stupid."

"You tried orienteering for the same reason, didn't you? Going for the runner's high?"

"Yeah. Coach never understood why I really did it. The medals are gathering dust in the basement. After that it was fasting and sleep deprivation. And exposing myself to cold. I tried drugs, too. They made me sick."

"And finally you come to us?"

He nodded. "I slept all day and stayed up all night. I wore black. I

lived like I thought a vampire should live. My parents kicked me out." Judas' eyes took on a mad glint of their own, and this time it was Brahms who shuddered — from pity. The madness in Judas' eyes was a desperate need to share a vision only he could see. A need to deal with the feeling that there was more to life than other people knew.

It was a feeling Brahms remembered well. The same need had driven him to spend more than one night awake at his piano, writing until his eyes stung. He looked at Judas again, this time searching for the ethereal play of colors that was the mortal's aura. It was there, yellow for idealism, gold for strong spirituality, and brown for frustration and bitterness, but as pale as if he had truly been a vampire.

"I just about gave up on that, too, but then..."

"You saw your first real vampire?"

"And tracked her down. Left a note for her to come and get me."

But Jeremiah came instead, Brahms guessed, maybe intending to kill the boy, but deciding to play with him first. Putting him through "tests" that would break him down and turn him into an animal. The Twelve Labors of Judas, an old Sabbat joke. He would become a vampire only after he had proven himself. But no one survived the tests.

Brahms reached out and touched Judas on the shoulder. "I saw Grosse Madeleine last night. She looks remarkably good for a woman who was supposed to have had her eye removed."

Judas started and probably would have run again, but this time Brahms held his arm. "Jeremiah has lied to you, Judas. There are more vampires than his pack, and not all of them are like him. Most of us

want to hunt down Jeremiah and kill him for the things he's done!" Most of us would have hunted you down and killed you if we had found your note. He tore himself from that thought. "How did you fake it?"

"Grosse Madeleine collects things like that. The eye was in a jar labelled 'Rasputin.' One seer is as good as another."

"Lucky." He let him go. "Could you have gone through with it if you had to take one of her eyes?"

"No." Judas bent down and picked up his jacket. He stared for a moment at the black-bladed knife of the Sabbat, then let the jacket drop to the ground. Brahms pulled off his own coat and put it around the mortal's shivering form. Judas met his gaze willingly this time. "So what are you going to do with me?"

"Do you still seek the Embrace?"

He thought about it. "No. I can't live your life. When it comes right down to it, I don't want it." He put his face in his hands, "I've failed again. But you know, this was closest I've ever gotten to feeling...."

"To your vision?"

"Yeah, that's right, to my vision. When I was trying to trick Jeremiah into making me a vampire, I felt it. When I was trying to be something I really wasn't."

Something he wasn't.... Brahms frowned and then grinned. "Judas, my boy, did Jeremiah ever tell you about the Masquerade?"

Just after dusk the next day, they stood together again, blending in with the rest of the crowd that stood watching the old factory burn. If the fire fighters were especially observant, they might have found a number of patches of light grey ash in the remains.

Judas took a last look at the scene and turned, walking away down the street. Brahms caught up a second later. "The Prince sends his thanks. We managed to destroy the entire pack, thanks to you. The Prince not only gave me permission, but ordered me to Embrace you," he said, as he hung a friendly arm around the young man's shoulders. "It seems you know too much about the Kindred to be allowed to remain mortal."

Judas laughed, with only a touch of strain in his voice. "You won't, will you?"

"Not unless you've changed your mind."

He shook his head, then sighed. "Do you realize that I managed to live up to my name after all?" He gestured back at the fire. "I betrayed them. Aren't you worried? That some day I'll betray you?"

Brahms pulled out a cigarette and lit it as he walked. "Not as long as we can keep you happy being something you aren't." He snapped his lighter shut and stuck it back in his pocket. He wondered how the Prince and the primogen council would react when he presented them with his neonate. Not a vampire, not even a ghoul, but a mortal. His heart was still beating, but he was a natural actor, and his aura was not that of a normal mortal. Judas was anything but normal, and that was the trick. He would become Brahms' greatest piece of work. The Masquerade in reverse.

He blew his smoke out in one long, steady stream. Breathing life into the night air.

CHAPTER TWO
BOOK OF NOD

✦

The earliest history of the Kindred is said to be recorded in the legendary *Book Of Nod*. Named for the land east of Eden where Caine first traveled, it chronicles the tumultuous birth of the bloodlines and the origins of the Jyhad, the war between the clans.

◆

In the beginning there was only Caine.

Caine who murdered his brother out of anger.

Caine who was cast out.

Caine who was cursed forever with immortality.

Caine who was cursed with the lust for blood.

It is Caine from whom we all come,

Our Sire's Sire.

◆

For the passing of an age he lived in solitude,

In loneliness and suffering.

For an eon he remained alone.

But the passing of memory drowned his sorrow.

And so he returned to the world of mortals,

To the world his brother and his brother's children had created.

He returned and was made welcome.

The people saw his power and worshipped him,

Making him King of their great City,

The First City, a place by the name of Enoch.

✦

Though he became ruler of a mighty nation, he was still alone,

For none were as he. His sorrow grew once again.

Then he committed another great sin, for he begat Progeny,

Of which there were only three.

But from them came more Progeny, his grandchildren,

And then Caine said "An end to this crime. There shall be no
more."

And as Caine's word was the law, his Brood obeyed him.

✦

The city stood for many ages,

And become the center of a mighty Empire.

But then came the Deluge, a great Flood that washed over the
world.

The City was destroyed,

And its people along with it.

✦

Again Caine fell into great sorrow and went into solitude,

Becoming as a dog amidst the wastes,

And leaving his Progeny to their own ends.

They came to him and begged him to return,

To help them rebuild the City.

But he would not come with them,

Saying the Flood had been sent as punishment

For his having returned to the world of life

And subverting the true law.

✦

So they returned alone to what mortals were left

And announced that they were the new rulers.

Each created a Brood,

In order to claim the glory of Caine,

Yet they did not have his wisdom or restraint.

A great war was waged, the Elders against their Children,

And the Children slew their parents.

✦

The rebels then built a new city

And brought to it 13 tribes.

It was a beautiful city and its people worshipped them as gods.

They created new Progeny of their own,

The Fourth Generation of Cainites.

✦

But they feared the Jyhad,

And it was forbidden for those Children

To create others of their kind.

This power their Elders kept for themselves.

When a Childe was created, it was hunted down and killed,

And its Sire with it.

✦

Though this city was as great as Caine's, eventually it grew old.

As do all living things, it slowly began to die.

The gods at first did not see the truth,

And when they at last looked about them it was too late.

Their city was destroyed and their power extinguished,

And they were forced to flee, their Progeny along with them.

But many were killed in the flight, for they had grown weak.

With their authority gone, all were free to create their own Broods,

And soon there were many new Kindred,

Who ruled across the face of the Earth.

✦

But this could not last.

Over time, there came to be too many of the Kindred,

And then there was war once again.

The Elders were already deep in hiding,

For they had learned caution.

But their Children had founded their own cities and Broods,

And it is they who were killed in the great wave of war.

There was war so total, that there are none of that Generation

To speak of themselves any longer.

Waves of mortal flesh were sent across continents

In order to crush and burn the cities of the Kindred.

Mortals thought they were fighting their own wars,

But it is for us that they spilt their blood.

✦

Once this war was over,

All of the Kindred hid from one another

And from the humans that surrounded them.

In hiding we remain today,

For the Jyhad continues still.

◆

CHAPTER THREE
THE DAMNED

✦

To WH, from your most devoted servant,

Many years have passed and I fervently hope that time will have dulled somewhat the distressing memories you carry. I dare to send this in a spirit of supplication; while your forgiveness is too much to ask, I crave at least your understanding. I owe you some kind of explanation for the events which so shattered your blameless life.

Although I exhibited precious little Menschwert before you and your companions, the flame of humanitas still burns in my breast, albeit erratically. Time and nature both struggle to extinquish it, thus completing my descent into the inferno of madness and beastiality. I must guard my soul well — as well as any priest — for any lapse in vigilance lets in the beast, with results which you yourself have seen.

I know it is impossible to atone, an eternity of pious prayer is too short a time. However, as a mark of penitence I offer you the enclosed document, the act of which makes me a traitor to my own kind. I pray you may find something in its pages to help you understand the torment I inflicted upon you, and by understanding, perhaps, dispell some little amount of the pain. The tone, I fear, is somewhat dry; a soldier has little need for pleasing tricks of poesy to beguile a reader. I have merely set down that which I know, as well as I may.

I owe you a debt which can never be discharged. If at any time I may be of service to you or your family, I am at your command.

Semper Servus,

$\mathcal{VT}$

Where to begin? So much ink has been spilled down the centuries. I am constantly amazed by the regularity with which you mortals stumble across truths and half-truths — sometimes very profound ones — by the most haphazard and fallacious thinking; and then, unaware of what you have uncovered, proceed to expound generalities of entirely the wrong order.

We are monsters to thee, yet heroes as well. We are the incarnations of dark metaphors and suppressed desires, yet we are also the nobility of fairy tales, beloved of children. We are a baseless superstition, an artistic genre, a psychological condition, a yearning made flesh, an externalization of a guilt-lust-violence complex, and many other things beside.

✦

OUR
TRUE
NATURE

Some two and a half centuries ago, a French churchman named Calmet sought to collect all the information *extant* on the nature of vampires. It is not surprising, then, that his treatise contains many contradictions and areas of uncertainty. Quoting from the reports of Papal Commissions sent out to deal with 'plagues' of vampires in Austria, Hungary, Moravia and Silesia, he reported that a vampire may be destroyed by being transfixed with a wooden stake, followed by decapitation and the burning of the remains. This will indeed destroy a vampire, just as certainly as it would destroy a mortal. Such a clever man, Calmet.

Motion pictures have abbreviated this treatment somewhat, creating the fallacy that the stake is sufficient. Do not believe such tales. Transfixing its heart on a stake will immobilize a vampire, but some further treatment is necessary *terminus sit*. Whether this be burning or sunlight, *ist egal*; but trust not the stake alone. Neither should you place your faith in weapons of metal, as did your American friend. Such things injure, but the wounds heal quickly — else I should not be writing now.

Sunlight, it is said, is infallible doom to my kind. Motion pictures show motley greasepaint vampires crumbling to dust at Sol's caress, or bursting into flames like those doused with Greek Fire. Sadly, this is true, if somewhat overstated. Sunlight burns our skin as does flame, and only the oldest and strongest can withstand it for long.

Thus we must sleep during the day and act only at night. During the day we are very sluggish, and find it difficult to do anything besides sleep. Only those of us who have not left our human nature very far behind are capable of taking action when the sun is in the sky. I myself have not seen the light of day in many centuries, and have nearly forgotten the gleam of the sun's golden rays. But I do not miss it.

Crosses, holy water, and the other trappings of religion may be ignored — the Church is the first refuge of mortals faced by things beyond their comprehension, especially in former times. *Ipso dicto*, however, I have seen rare occasions where such items were capable of

causing considerable discomfort — their wielder almost glowed with faith in the Divinity, and I can only conclude that the religious items served somehow to channel the power of that faith. Ignore the tricks of the cinema, however, with their crossed candlesticks and shadows of windmills' sails.

The reputed properties of garlic, aconite and other herbs are likewise mere superstition. They repel vampires no more than they do mortals, for all the canting of the goodwives who peddle them. Like the Church, the village wisewoman was oft required to use her 'magic' against vampires, and was just as successful.

Film-makers have made other fallacious legends part of the common parlance. For instance, we can see our own reflections in the mirror, though some of us pretend otherwise in honor of the great cinematic tradition. Likewise, we can appear on film. Indeed, some of my kind have appeared in movies, and one was even a director of no little repute.

It is equally ludicrous to presume that a vampire would not be able to travel about as he would like. We Cainites (one of our race's terms for ourselves, like Kindred, the origin of which I shall later discuss) may enter any house and home we please at any time. It is likewise preposterous to think a vampire would not be able to cross running water. Indeed, water affects us not at all. We no longer breathe, hence we cannot drown. While being trapped underwater is unpleasant and may, if prolonged, result in some physical deterioration, no vampire has died of immersion alone, although some bloodlines are rumored to have a weakness *vis-a-vis* water. Belike this is how many of the rumors originated, for weaknesses have arisen in several bloodlines and have been passed down from Sire to Get.

The cinematic vampire, it seems, may take several forms if the human shape suits not his purpose: wolf, bat, mist — in some legends, cat and night-bird also. The powers of the Elders are considerable, and they are seldom found in those of later generation. I have seen many wonders during my brief and unwilling involvement in their game of Jyhad, and I no longer discount the stories of shape-shifting. But I tell you this — a vampire who has plural forms will either be of a rare breed, the Gangrel clan, or will be very old, very wise and very powerful. I pray that such a one will never cross your path.

Many of us, however, have abilities which a mortal would consider supernatural. As predators, our senses are sharp, and some have developed other talents to aid in the hunt. One example — the ability to inspire fear, stillness, obedience and other emotional responses — is a useful one, although popular writers have embellished it somewhat in the interests of their stories.

◆

THE
GHOULS

It occurs to me that some of the confusion about a vampire's supernatural powers and weaknesses may be due to mistaken identity. There exists a class of creature in between mortal and vampire, which the Kindred (the other of our self-referential sobriquets, and the most popular) have named Ghoul. It is not the legendary corpse-eating *ghûl* of the Indies, although certain individuals may display similar behavior.

Mortals who drink the blood of the Kindred without first being drained will become Ghouls. These creatures may go abroad in daylight as other mortals do, but they do not suffer the Hunger, nor do they age as long as they feed on vampiric blood regularly. They may even have superhuman strength and reflexes. From time to time, it is advantageous to create such servants, commanding their loyalty through the promise of eternal life. They need not even be human — a hound that has drunk of one's blood becomes the most perfect and faithful guardian one could desire. Thus do tales of hell-hounds arise.

While Ghouls display some of the strengths of the vampire, they retain most of the weaknesses of the mortal. Impalement will slay Ghouls as effectively as mortals, and a lead bullet will kill as surely as a silver one. They may even develop a fear of religious trappings, or garlic, or what you will — a purely neurotic phenomenon, based on the fact that they *believe* these things can harm them. The existence of Ghouls in animal form may partially explain the widespread belief in shape-changing vampires.

Some Ghouls may well believe themselves full-fledged vampires, having been deceived to that end by their creators. They may even act according to their mistaken ideas — to the point of drinking blood — for they seldom understand the ways of the Kindred any better than mortals. Most are deranged to some extent by the experiences they have suffered — witness, *zum Beispiel*, your late husband's employer — and many are deliberately misinformed by their masters, the better to serve them.

✦

THE
EMBRACE

Mortal superstitions deal at great length with the means by which a vampire may come into existence. These range from the predictably religious to the utterly bizarre, and can make an entertaining evening's reading if one is so inclined. Other than entertainment, however, they serve little purpose.

The first and most common of these myths is the legend that anyone bitten by a vampire will himself become a vampire. Thus, each time a vampire feeds, it creates another of its kind. One wonders how it is that any mortals are left in the world. Furthermore, a corpse may become a vampire if it was a suicide, an oathbreaker, a member of a tainted bloodline, or *de tout*, an evil person. Again, the globe would be peopled with nothing but vampires — and I tell you this, I have not seen this army of undead.

Indeed, to my understanding, there are not many of us upon this globe. To my knowledge, there is only one means through which a mortal may become a vampire. Shame fills me again when I recall that I intended this fate for you, and I rejoice that Providence denied me. Truly do I repent the eternity of sorrow which so nearly was your destiny.

There is a grain of truth in the legend *de gustando*. To become a vampire, one must lose all one's mortal blood — but that is only part of the horror. *Mortui exsanguinati mortui veri*, if nothing further is done; the fang will kill as everlastingly as the blade or the bullet.

As mortality stands on the brink of extinction, as the flesh slowly dies, the vampire assailant may choose to spare the victim from death or deny Heaven's grace, for all is one *his rebus*. By replacing the stolen mortal blood with a little of the vampire's own, a Progeny is created. But a single drop of blood upon the lips of the dying arouses him sufficiently to drink from the wrist of his Sire.

How can I express the horror of the Embrace? The fear and confusion? The revulsion and terror? The pain? Even the passing of centuries has not dulled the memory.

Understand that I am no coward. As a soldier, I endured the privations of the camp, the perils of battle, the savagery of the victor, of which I plead guilty to my share, for such was the *Zeitsmode*. But even those things I witnessed as a prisoner of the Turks could not have prepared me for the experience of being hurled into this cursed half-life.

I was, *de gratia potestates descriptis*, in a most peaceful state of mind as my blood was stolen. As deaths go — and I have seen many kinds — this was surely the least distressing. It was as though my experience was a strange and somewhat unsettling dream. Far off in the warm, soft darkness of my failing mind, I became aware of a light; I knew that this was where I must go, and I knew that, once I arrived there, all would be well with me. I began to drift toward it.

Abruptly the welcoming light was extinguished. My face felt an impact like a musket-ball, and as I tried to scream, my mouth filled with liquid fire. The vitriol seared my throat and stomach; consciousness returned as though it would rend me limb from limb. A thousand fishhooks tore my flesh in every direction.

47

I prayed for death — anything to stop the pain — but I could not even lapse from consciousness. *Nec Turcos, nec Inquaesitores* ever commanded such torment. Magnify a thousandfold the sting of vinegar on a cut finger, and flood the feeling through every limb and every vein. Add to this the gnawing, starving ache of five days' forced march without food or water. Deny sleep, swooning or any other surcease from the all-consuming *dolor*. But no. My meager wordsmithing can convey nothing of it.

I knew only that I must drink, and as I did so the pain abated a little. My eyes cleared, and I saw what it was that I drank.

My first reaction was denial. This could not possibly be happening. Even in the fifteenth century, men of education and breeding scoffed at the superstitions of the peasant. As a child, my nurses had frightened me to sleep with stories of the terrible *vrolok*, but I had outgrown such tales long before. This was a nightmare, an hallucination of some kind. I tried to focus on thoughts of meat, fruit, wine — but to no avail. Blood was all. Blood was reality. All else was discarded.

I can only be thankful that I was in a remote place. Had I been Embraced in a city, with people all around, there is no telling what havoc might have ensued. The Hunger blotted out reason entirely. Had my own son appeared before me then, he would have died to feed the Hunger, for I was utterly enslaved to it. No opium fiend in a Limehouse or Shanghai den was ever so helplessly, so wretchedly dependent.

I cry for mercy. The memory — and the recollection of what followed — distresses me, and I shall not continue the narrative. Instead, I shall address another, but related, topic.

✦

ANATOMIA
VAMPIRICA

Though our external appearance remains much like that of the living, there are those among us who insist that the Change transforms its subject into another species — *Homo Sapiens Sanguineus*, *Homo Sapientissimus*, and *Homo Vampiricus* have all been advanced as names for this new race, following the Swedish classification.

Be that as it may, it seems beyond dispute that the body undergoes as much of a change as the psyche. As will become apparent, much of what follows is — and can only be — conjecture, unsupported by dissection.

The gross physical changes are a matter of common knowledge, so much so that we have allowed them to remain in popular fiction. The canine teeth are indeed long and pointed, the better to draw blood. However, they are only fully extended at the time of the kill, being at other times withdrawn into their sockets by the contraction of a flexible tissue at their base. Both speech and secrecy would be most difficult otherwise. Some lack the means to withdraw their teeth, but they are easily discovered and are a dying clan.

To feed, we merely need to bite, retract the teeth from the wound, and begin to drink. If we lick the wound after we drink, then no trace of our feeding will remain. Indeed, if we lick any wound which we have caused with our claws or fangs, we can heal it completely.

Our own skin, as with the cinematic vampire, is invariably pale. Partly, it seems, this stems from our aversion to sunlight, but it is also due to our arrested state of death. *Darüber noch später.*

Our Hunger is a drive for sustenance, of that there can be no doubt. From this, and from bitter experiences with the foods I most enjoyed in my breathing days, it appears that the inward parts of the vampire have lost their facility for digestion. One seldom sees a stout vampire, and nearly all remark on a newfound slenderness after the Change. Being no longer required, the organs presumably wither.

The vampire's body remains as it was at the time of death. Hair and nails continue to grow for a few days, as they do on a fresh cadaver, but that is all. If I wish my hair or nails to be shorter, I must cut them each evening after I rise. It is my conjecture that the body of the vampire is actually dead, and is only arrested from the natural process of decay by the power of the Change. The skin becomes a little tighter over the bones, much as it does in the newly dead.

The lungs of a vampire no longer breathe — though many have learned to feign breathing while among the living — for the fresh blood of the prey provides the small amount of oxygen needed to sustain the dead tissues in their stasis. Only a young or foolish vampire takes blood from the jugular vein, where it is near the end of its journey and full of impurities; the blood of the carotid artery is clean and wholesome, and much to be preferred.

Just as the lungs no longer breathe, so the heart no longer beats. The blood of prey somehow suffuses through the body by a process of osmosis, rather than flowing along veins and arteries. This can be seen in the fact that when a vampire weeps — which indeed we do, and more often than a mortal might suppose — the tears themselves are of blood. Cut a vampire's throat, and you will find the vessels empty. The closure and atrophy of those blood vessels nearest the skin is another reason for the pallid complexion which marks the vampire, although a rosy hue is noticeable after feeding.

The blood of the prey, coupled with the blood of the Sire, does appear to have some remarkable properties. We are able to heal ourselves of most wounds with remarkable quickness. We still feel pain, and a reflex sends blood to the afflicted area — just as in life, blood will suffuse bruised tissue and colour it purple. The one exception to this rule is the stake so beloved of writers and film-makers. This will induce a kind of paralysis or trance, although it will not kill in its own right. Quite why this is so is unknown to me, for the heart no longer beats and so is not necessary to pump the flow of blood. I have heard various mystical explanations of this phenomenon, but must confess myself at a loss to explain it rationally.

The body no longer makes and replenishes its own blood, and relies entirely on prey for fresh blood and the nutrients which Science has found blood to carry. Something in the blood of the Sire, passed down through the Change, fans the spark of Life and arrests decay, but regular infusions of fresh blood are needed lest decay begin again. And when a vampire *is* destroyed, that decay is fantastically swift, as though Time were recalling the debt of decades or centuries. Nothing remains but dust, which is why anatomical study is impossible and so much must be guessed.

We are able to heal our wounds using this blood upon which we feed. We are able to use it to regenerate whole limbs and organs, given time and need. Regeneration always restores us to the physical state we possessed when we died, including hair length, face shape, body weight — everything. When the body is injured, it will reform itself in the same mold again and again. We are already dead, and so cannot die except through the forces of life — the eternal sun and the primordial flame.

One last question remains *in re corporis* — a somewhat prurient one, which I shall answer with as much delicacy as I may. Through the popular entertainments, the vampire has become established as a highly potent figure of romance — and betimes of more than romance. While the act of love is physically possible for a vampire of either sex, the associated impulses, drives and responses have died along with the flesh — which, incidentally, is cold to the touch rather than warm. By effort of will we may go through the motions, forcing blood to the relevant areas in the same way as healing a wound, but that is all. The ecstasy of the Kiss replaces all such needs within us. Blood is the only object of our desire.

✦

THE
HUNGER

To live as a vampire is to live with horror. Always squatting on one's shoulder like a warlock's fiend is the knowledge of the Hunger. And always, always, does it approach — sometimes slowly and surreptitiously, sometimes with great haste, but always ravenously. The Hunger can never fully be satiated.

Hunger, we call it, but the term is woefully inadequate. Mortals know hunger, even starvation, but this is as nothing. The Hunger replaces almost every need, every drive known to the living — food, drink, reproduction, ambition, security — and it is more compelling than all of them combined.

More than a drive, it is a drug, one to which we are born with a hopeless addiction. In the taking of blood lies not only our survival, but also a pleasure beyond description. The Hunger is a physical, mental and spiritual ecstasy which throws all the pleasures of mortal life into shadow.

To be a vampire is to be trapped by the Hunger. The Beast may only be kept subdued by the greatest effort of will; to deny the Hunger enrages the Beast, until nothing may keep it in check. Thus we must commit monstrous acts to stop ourselves from becoming monsters — that is the Riddle. *Monsters we are, lest monsters we become.*

That is the paradox of our life. It is the curse of my own.

✦

THE
BEAST

The Beast rages constantly for release, and only the strongest will may hold it back. Sometimes it breaks its bonds, and runs riotous until it is recaptured. The strain of self-control, and the shameful memories of failed control, are hard enough to bear. Worse still is the knowledge, constant as the Hunger, that these things will surely happen again. Over the decades and centuries, this awareness gnaws at the mind like a rat at a ship's cable.

To be a vampire is to live on the edge of madness. Obsessive devotion to some self-appointed task can help keep despair from the mind, and if the task is one of great goodness, it is possible to reason that the end justifies the means. Some deliberately cultivate addictions, such as gambling or collecting art. Others shut themselves away and confine their hunting to a small, sparsely-populated area, telling themselves that they are protecting the rest of the world. These things can perhaps delay the onset of madness, but they can also provide it with its first foothold.

Ultimately, hard as we may strive against it, madness awaits us. The flame of Humanity ebbs and sputters until finally it is extinguished. Then the Beast is victorious, and monsters we become in truth. The Beast resides within the heart, and directs us toward evil, but when it overtakes the halls of the soul, then shall we *be* evil.

Some speak of *Golconda*, the vampire's Salvation. Both mortal and Kindred lore deny us Heaven's grace, but in Golconda we look for surcease from the Riddle. It is a stasis, where an individual may balance the Man and the Beast against each other so that striving is no longer needful. The descent into madness is halted, and although the individual is no longer recognizable as human in his thoughts and deeds, what remains of *Humanitas* is safe. In almost five centuries, I have met a meager few Kindred who have reached this blessed state, but all desire it as mortals desire Heaven.

✦

THE
BURDENS
OF
IMMORTALITY

We are, as the most cursory student of folklore knows, ageless and immortal. In this case, lore and tradition have the right of it. Once made, a vampire lives until actively destroyed, or until the Beast wins over the Man, or until, after countless millennia, the Blood is exhausted.

Down the centuries, mortals have hungered for the secret of immortality, thinking it would give them great power. From the priests of heathen times through the alchemists of my own breathing days and down to the physicians of the present, mortals have expended more wealth and effort in the war against aging and death than in the cause of any religion or trade.

Many newly made Kindred — myself included — rejoice in the thought of immortality when they first overcome the shock of the Change and begin to reconcile themselves to their new situation. Yet it is a barbed gift, and another door by which madness may enter in.

Consider, for example, having to watch your loved ones — even your children and grandchildren — grow old and die, while you remain strong and vigorous. There is a necessity to live completely outside mortal society, or at least to move on every decade or so, lest it be noticed that you do not age. The tide of history flows over you like a stream, leaving you unchanged.

The longer one lives as a vampire, the greater the sense of detachment from mortal affairs. It can be an advantage at first, helping to deaden the guilt of killing and the pain of losing one's mortal family to remorseless Time. But as detachment grows, *Humanitas* wanes, and the Beast grows stronger. The most terrible of mortal serial killers often are detached from their kind, *atrocitates tranquilliter gestandae*. It is the same face on a different coin, as the Turks would say.

Even if one can fight off this dehumanizing *verschiedenskeit*, Time lends madness other weapons. For without detachment, guilt and remorse may work unchecked, eating at the feelings like acid eating metal. Mortal soldiers return from foreign wars wounded by the violence they have seen and done, yet they have only to live with their memories for a few brief decades. A vampire's guilt is eternal, and time can sap the strongest will. Another face of the Riddle: we may lose our Humanity to avoid losing our minds, yet what is madness but lost Humanity? *Sooner or later*, grins the Beast, *you shall be mine*.

A further paradox — we grow stronger as we grow weaker. The older a vampire, the more powerful — the more cunning to have lived so long, the better versed and practiced in certain arts and powers, the better able to withstand those things that are anathema to us. And, perhaps, the stronger of will, not to have become a monster. Yet the weaker, for the Beast tries the bars of its prison ceaselessly, and in time they must yield. The oldest shut themselves away from the rest of their kind, fearing the day when they shall become monsters and distracting themselves with paranoid games of cat's-paw using younger Kindred as playing-pieces.

✦

VITA
SUB
TENEBRAS

There are other reasons for our nocturnal life besides the need to avoid the sun's rays. It is so much easier to stalk and hunt in the hours of darkness. *Imprimis*, the prey is usually dulled by fatigue — and betimes drink — and can see little in the poor light. The hunter, on the other hand, is normally fresh and fully rested, and can often see as well as a mortal does at noonday. *Secundus*, the hours of darkness are less populous, and promise fewer interruptions. Feeding is a vulnerable time; the Beast is near the surface, and may stand at bay rather than leave a kill. This has been the undoing of more than one Neonate.

✦

THE ORIGINS OF THE KINDRED

Like mortals, we have our own history and lore, by which we seek to explain our existence and understand our place in the world. Just as the veracity of your legends is lost in the shrouds of history, so is the truth of our lore uncertain. However, over the years I have unearthed a number of different sources, and through painstaking study, I believe I have arrived at some semblance of fact and truth.

Most of our lore is contained within an ancient text known as the *Book of Nod*. Neither any of my acquaintances nor I has ever seen or heard of a complete copy, although fragments have been unearthed over the centuries, *multis linguis, multis causis*. There is much confusion and contradiction, and some versions appear to have been deliberately falsified.

Over the centuries, I have been fortunate to peruse fragments in Greek, Turkish, Aramaic, Latin and *Hebraica Quabalistica*, as well as translations from Old Kingdom hieroglyphics and Assyrian cuneiform. Inconsistencies are rife, but the main body of the tale states that my kind is descended from Caine, whom some call The Third Mortal.

Outcast from mortal society for the killing of his brother, Caine was cursed with eternal life and a craving for blood. We, his children, are the heirs to that curse, condemned to repeat his crime endlessly.

Caine wandered in the wilderness until his name was all but forgotten. He returned to the world of mortals and was able to establish himself as the ruler of a city, by the name of Enoch, Uniech, Enkil or what you will. Many Kindred call it the First City. Here, Caine created three Progeny — those whom we call the Second Generation. They in turn begot the Third Generation, who are numbered at nine, twenty-seven, one hundred or none at all, according to the source one reads. Caine forbade the creation of any further Kindred, perhaps having gained some understanding of what he had unleashed upon the world. There is no word of any Kindred establishing Caine's rule elsewhere, and if they all remained in the First City, their increasing numbers must have strained the mortal population.

All was tranquil in Caine's domain until a great flood destroyed the city. Caine saw this as divine punishment for returning to the world of mortals, and resumed his wanderings, leaving his Progeny to their own devices. Though he forbade them to create more, they ignored his imperative as each of his Progeny desired a Brood of its own.

No more is heard of our ancestor, although from time to time, a vampire calling himself Caine will appear in some part of the world or another. Occasionally, he is revealed as an impostor, but more often he vanishes as suddenly as he appeared. Some believe that Caine still lives, while others — myself included — think it more likely to be some subterfuge of the Elders. It is said that Caine is rent with sorrow for having unleashed such misery and suffering upon the world.

Once free of Caine's restrictions, the Second and Third Generations created a great multitude of Progeny. They ruled together briefly, but all was not calm between them. Eventually, the youngest Generations rose and slew their Sires, drinking their blood. This Fourth Generation built another great city (some sources hint that it might have been Babylon, while others suggest that it rests somewhere beneath the sands of Egypt) which we know only as the Second City.

The rule of these new vampires was not untroubled, for certain Kindred of the Third Generation still lived. Indeed, some say they were secretly behind the slayings of their Elders. It was decreed that they alone reserved the right to beget Progeny, and that any of the Fourth Generation who disobeyed them were to be hunted down and killed along with their Sires. Though the Fourth Generation lived in public, the Third Generation, whom we know today as the Antediluvians, lived in secret and revealed to no one the location of their havens. For nearly two millennia (some say 23 centuries), the Fourth Generation ruled the city, while the Third Generation ruled them. Eventually, the culture grew decadent and the city died. In a great uprising, the people rose up and killed all the Kindred they could find.

When the Second City fell, its rulers fled. Scattered far and wide, they were too numerous and too widespread for the hidden Elders of the Third Generation to threaten them, and thus was begot the Fifth Generation. The Kindred grew in numbers and settled in all parts of the world.

Mortal history records a time, beginning over two thousand years ago, of burgeoning empires locked in combat with one another — the time of the Persians, the Greeks and the Tartars. Thus did the Fifth Generation establish its own order. Meanwhile, the Antediluvians lay hidden and pursued their own mad schemes. This age of wars may even have been of their making, the beginning of their great Jyhad. Whatever the truth, almost none remain to speak of it. I myself have met only one of the Fifth Generation, and at the time I did not know it.

It is said by some that near the end of this period, the Antediluvians emerged from their hiding places and sucked the blood of all my kind, each leaving but one new Progeny of their line. This legend has it that this was the close of the Second Cycle, that the Antediluvians' lust for blood was so great that they needed all of my race as their Vessels.

Those who believe in the Cycle legends predict an Armageddon in the near future. They say that the Antediluvians are asleep now, but someday they will awaken and then they will feed. The Third Cycle is coming to a close, and none but the Third Generation will remain alive at its conclusion. The true believers say that each Cycle lasts 2300 years, and soon, very soon, the time approaches. They call it Gehenna, and some prepare for it fervently. As a man of science, these beliefs seem extreme to me, but they cannot be entirely discounted.

Whatever the truth of the matter, I know that the Elders of the Fifth and older Generations exist in complete seclusion. Those of the Inconnu fear one another that much. To have lived this long, they must be cunning and powerful, and they may be expected to cover their tracks well. This leaves my own Sixth Generation and its descendants as the bulk of the visible Kindred. I have heard claims of a Thirteenth or Fourteenth Generation, but prefer to dismiss them. Such creatures must be very weak and close to mortality, for it is said that the Blood thins as it is passed from one generation to the next.

✦

THE
MASQUERADE

In 1435, there was founded an organization, a cause, an obsession, a war. Call it what you will; history knows it as the Inquisition. Besides burning harmless old women and excommunicating French field mice for eating farmers' wheat, this Inquisition did betimes achieve its aim, and cleansed the world of no few true witches, warlocks and monsters. Many such monsters were Kindred, and the diligent Inquisitors traced whole bloodlines and put all to the flame.

For the first time, our kind stood in real danger of extinction. Superstitious belief coupled with scientific thoroughness placed in mortal hands the wherewithal to rid the world of monsters forever. It was a terrifying time — as insane to us as the Holocaust which mortals visited on one another earlier in this century. Those Kindred who survived bear the mental scars of the Inquisition to this day, and many live a life of paranoid seclusion, dealing with the breathing world as little as possible.

Before this time, we had lived more or less openly, relying on our power and position to preserve us. Though we did not announce our presence, we did not struggle to hide it either. We had grown proud in

our power, and the fall which followed was terrible indeed.

The survivors quickly learned the wisdom of stealth and secrecy, and networks sprang up as they do among mortals in times of crisis, conveying information and individuals *sub rosa* for the safety of all. This was the birth of what may be called a Vampiric society.

The name *Camarilla* arose for this organization, reflecting the small, secret rooms used for meeting and concealment. Groups made contact with one another, united for the first time by this adversity.

The first global convocation took place in 1486. Many chose to absent themselves, but this meeting gave itself the power to speak for all Kindred existing or yet to be made, and to pass laws governing all. The founders of the Camarilla made themselves its lawmakers. The first such law, and the most sacred, is that of the Masquerade. It is this law which I willingly violate by laying these pages before you.

The horrors of the preceding decades had taught us the need for secrecy and shown us that, after all, we were vulnerable. It was vital, therefore, that the breathing world be convinced it had killed the last of us, or, better yet, that we had never existed at all. We had to match organization with organization and cause with cause if we hoped to survive.

The Masquerade had two faces, each with a number of contingencies and lesser objectives. *Imprimis simplicissimusque*, reasonable secrecy and care was required of all Kindred. Nothing must betray our continued existence, and any individual who broke this secrecy would be outcast and hunted down as a danger to all.

Secundus, active steps must be taken to change the character of mortal society, and direct minds away from superstitious thoughts.

Many of the Kindred had turned to scholarship to beguile the lonely decades, and certain matters were made available to the *Taggänger* in the fields of alchemy, literature, art, geography, cosmology *und so weiter*. Many mortals were already turning their steps in this direction, so the task was not unduly arduous. Names spring to mind such as Bacon, Dee, Galileo, Copernicus, Ariosto, Michelangelo, da Vinci, Cellini, and Columbus. It was a brave Age we made.

With so many fresh discoveries clamouring for attention, the mortals lost their single-mindedness in chasing monsters. A little later — principally due to an alliance of French Methuselahs — material and political philosophies were influenced. Science had bred Reason, and Reason denied monsters. Over the following centuries, we were able to crush superstition almost completely. No one of any education seriously believed we had ever existed.

Adjustments continued over the decades — a war here, a discovery there to keep breathing minds focused away from us. We have had a hand in some of the most significant events in history. Do not, however, think that all your history is our work, for marionettes you are not and have never been. Marx was of your kind, and no vampire could have formulated his thoughts. Brief decades later, monstrous deeds were performed in Europe, but none of my kind were involved. Those monsters were entirely your own.

Not long ago, mortal minds turned once more to the mystical — though the greatest mystery to me is the appeal of the music which was born in those days — and superstition briefly waxed ascendant. The knowledge of certain chemical substances was made available, and many inquisitive minds were distracted or forever silenced.

Throughout this last century, steps have been taken to preserve the image of the vampire in popular entertainments, for thus it may be seen more clearly as a fiction. The Masquerade is unraveling, as the mysticism of the mortals increases. The Camarilla struggles to turn back the tide — the evidence of that is all around you.

✦

CHILDER

Comical as it may seem, there is a generation gap among vampires just as there is in mortal society. The younger vampires — primarily those Embraced in the latter half of this century and those of the most recent generations — include an element which chafes at the restrictions of Kindred society and laws. Like rebellious adolescents, these "anarchs," as they call themselves, demand their freedom and ignore the effects on the rest of their kind. They would create their own Broods without restraint, deny the authority of Princes, break the laws of the Masquerade, and do a hundred other things which would force the knowledge of our existence upon the mortal world.

The Elders, and many other Kindred, do not take kindly to this attitude, and in some places a virtual state of war exists between them. Some see this as a sign of the end of the current Cycle, and speak of our imminent extinction.

These anarchs do not believe that they are being told the truth by the Elders, and they know that they are not being told all about their situation. The Elders do not trust the anarchs, fearing that they seek to slay them.

✦

THE
WORLD
OF
THE
UNDEAD

On one level, the world of the vampire is the world of mortals. A vampire moves in the world of mortals much as a nobleman moves in the forest of beasts while hunting. Just as the noble has his castles and courts, however, so the vampire has a world of his own, where he may consort with his own kind.

Some vampires shun the society of their Kindred, but such society exists, paralleling mortal society in both function and form. Just as there are mortal rulers and mortal societies in the world's great cities, so too there are vampire Clans and Princes.

Most Kindred seek Princedom, for it is the only means by which to create a Brood of one's own. Princes do not often allow others to create Progeny, and even if they do, they are allowed to create only one. A Prince may create as many Progeny as he wishes and their loyalty adds to his strength.

It would be fatuous to list and describe every Clan, Prince and Fief in the world. Suffice it to say that every mortal city of any size supports a vampire population, and these populations are organized in a number of different ways. Some rule collectively, others autocratically, but all rule and all resent intrusion. Like organized criminals and law enforcement agencies, they have structured their

Domain to their liking and suppress anything which threatens to disturb their peace.

Accordingly, a vampire who enters a new city is required by *höflichkeit* to make himself known to its rulers and satisfy them that their rule is not threatened or challenged. To fail in this courtesy is to invite war. No witch-hunter ever pursues his prey so diligently as a Clan or Prince seeks out a stranger *nouveau arrivé*.

Most rulers, I have said, are content to keep the peace in their Fief and pursue their own arcane ends. But there are exceptions. One is the league of Clans which calls itself the Sabbat, or the Black Hand. Their Fief extends across the eastern half of North America, and they are everything that mortals expect of monstrous vampires. Reveling in the violent, the perverse and the bestial, they are shunned by their own kind, and woe betide the incautious vampire whom they find in their territory.

Above the Clans stands the Camarilla. All vampires are aware of this league, and all are invited to join. To take an analogy *ex mundo vivantis* — if a Fief is a regional or national government, then the Camarilla is the League of Nations. To my mind, it is equally effective, but some set great store by its infrequent convocations. Certainly the Elders of the Council are not to be underestimated as individual powers — most are very old and all are very powerful. Primarily it enforces the ancient Traditions, most important among them the Masquerade, so soon enough I may have cause to test its resolve and strength.

The Clans all have their various alliances and oppositions, which shift as often and widely as those of the small countries of the mortal world. I have mentioned the protocols which must be observed when entering a Fief as an outsider. These obligations and structures are no more than protocols, and may be broken from time to time; but there is a stronger bond — stronger even than the ties of blood kinship — whose *auctoritas* is absolute. It is the mystic tie we call the Oath, or the Blood Bond.

I have touched upon the power of Blood to create new Kindred and Ghouls. Its effect on Kindred is no less powerful. It is said to be the sweetest blood in the world, but it creates a potent bond between donor and drinker. A vampire who drinks another vampire's blood on three separate occasions becomes trapped in a blood kinship as strong as that between Sire and Get; in fact, many Sires force this bond upon their unknowing Get at the time of creation, the better to command their loyalty. Among the Kindred, the Oath is a most potent bond; to take the Oath is to give over one's mind and heart to another, and a willing Oath is never undertaken lightly. If all else fails and you have no other means of defence against a vampire, use my name — the chance is slender, but if your attacker happens to be Blood Bound to me, then you shall be safe.

✦

DIABLERIE

By now, if my labours have been equal to my intent, it will be apparent to you that the society of the Kindred is as diverse as that of the living. We have our princes and paupers, our dreamers and men of action, our heroes and criminals, our idealists and our perverts. The matter I am about to disclose is little more than speculation, but increasingly I am inclined to believe the rumours.

I have said how the blood of the Sire empowers the blood of the prey, so that the body is sustained in its unlife. According to rumour, the blood of the Sire loses this power with the passing of centuries and millennia, and an exceptionally aged vampire must needs drink the blood of Kindred to survive. Although the decay of a mortal cadaver is spared us, time still takes a toll, and the Blood is not absolutely immortal. A young vampire of an early generation is able to subsist on the blood of animals, but as the centuries pass — or as the blood thins with transmission — first animal and then mortal blood loses its ability to sustain.

The Antediluvians are said to prey on the Kindred as we do on mortals, and there is no end to the stories of their depravity. Increasingly, though, rumours spread of younger Kindred doing likewise. The reason for this is unclear. Perhaps the youngest generations bear so little of the Blood that it serves them only for a few centuries, or perhaps they seek the powers of the Antediluvians by imitating their ways. I have long wondered if this is the cause of the war among my kind, the Jyhad which has lasted so long. The Antediluvians hide, for they fear that they will be killed by those seeking their blood and thus their power. The Elders fear the anarchs, for they fear that they shall be eaten by them as well. The anarchs fear all those who are older than they, for they know that they are prey to a most deadly predator. The conflict between my kind is a cannibalistic and horrific war indeed.

I have already mentioned the Oath, which is undertaken by drinking the blood of another vampire (usually one's Sire or Prince).

It is known that taking the blood of one's own Get carries no such bond, and it seems also that the Antediluvians — and those others who habitually prey on their own kind — are able to do so without creating any kind of bond or obligation. This fact, more than anything, makes the practice of Diablerie (as it has come to be known) a shocking and perverted thing to the Kindred, and any vampire who is a known Diabolist may be killed out of hand by any who find him. The Diabolist must hunt with care, for he stalks the most dangerous game in the world. Doubtless some find a great exhilaration in this existence.

The Elders, needless to say, deny these rumours absolutely. To admit to such things would incite a revolution as terrible as the rising of the Fourth Generation. Yet there is evidence, which the diligent can find though the Antediluvians cover their tracks ever so carefully.

✦

LAST
PLEA

My discourse is at an end; my treachery complete. By now, I hope you will understand in some measure what impelled me to those acts I shall always rue and why I felt it necessary now to place this document before you. I cannot ask for your forgiveness — my crimes are too great. But if there be pity in your heart, pray for me.

You now know more about my kind than any mortal living — aye, even more than your friend the professor when he sought to destroy me. The use to which you put this knowledge I leave to your own conscience.

I have changed a great deal since we last met. For many years thereafter, I sought within myself for something inexpressible. Now, I believe I have found it, or am about to. If Golconda be truly within my reach, I may endure, for in the depths of introspection which prompted my writing, I have found a desire for *quietus* at any price. That was a partial reason for my discourse. I know full well that the knowledge I have imparted could lead to the destruction of myself and my kind. The will to live — if life this be — is too strong in any vampire to allow for a more direct suicide.

Whatever you decide, I wish you and yours well. I have followed the career of your son Quincy with great interest, and the lives of his children also. I rejoice that Fate stayed my beastly hand and ensured the welfare of your fine family. What a great comfort they must be to you.

In parting, may I presume to render my condolences on the regrettable death of your husband, of which I read in the *Times* of London. Your love for him is only too well-known to me. If the prayers of such a creature may be of any comfort, know that you have mine.

You shall hear no more from me unless you wish it. I say again, my service is yours to command. I can be reached through the personal columns of any major European newspaper; merely mention my name, and your own, and my retainers shall pass on your message to me.

Adieu.

Your most devoted and penitent servant,

V. T.

CHAPTER FOUR
STREETS OF BLOOD

✦

What is it like to live in a world of perpetual night? To dance under the blood-red moon? To lust for the blood of living, intelligent prey?

City life is as quicksilver as the Cainite itself. Long periods of peace can explode without warning into spasms of great strife and turmoil. The vampire is an animal of twisted emotion and instinct. One Kindred's obsessions and perversions can suddenly bring her into conflict with another. Though the Kindred can live with one another in peace for years, eventually the truce ends and the cannibalistic war begins anew. The Jyhad never truly ends — it only casts a smaller shadow for a time.

Normally, a balance is reached among the Kindred of a city, whether by formal or tacit agreement. Efforts are made to minimize conflict, though strife is often unavoidable. When conflict does occur, it is almost always hidden beneath the veil of the Masquerade, and rarely noticed by the mortals of the city. Thus may a war be waged without the elders fearing the return of the Inquisition.

Some Kindred take no part in the society of the Damned, and maintain no connection with others of their kind. They are known as the clanless, or the Caitiff. Cities are extremely large places and it is not difficult to isolate oneself from one's peers; indeed, it is said that the only Kindred who ever meet are the ones who wish to meet. However, sometimes even the most solitary vampires can be thrust into the politics of the day — in times of need, the Caitiff are mercilessly rooted out and questioned. The Justicars, enforcers of Kindred law, have been known to use solitary vampires as scapegoats for the crimes of others.

✦

CREATURES OF THE CITY

By agreement, though some say by nature, the vampire is a creature of the city. The wilds of the countryside are left to the werewolves and their ilk. This suits most Kindred. Why roam far and wide in search of sustenance when a few square blocks of even the smallest city provide more than enough vessels?

Younger Kindred sometimes feel the need to roam, but that desire usually fades as they age. Older Cainites are more likely to have become comfortable in single locations and make their havens at those spots. Those who do choose to wander the countryside will almost invariably come into contact with the Lupines, and the hatred between werewolves and Kindred runs deep.

Thus the city has become a gilded prison for the Kindred. Though cities are the center of civilization, and in this day and age often cover enormous expanses of terrain, they are still cells from which the Kindred are unable to escape. They are trapped in both body and spirit. Imprisonment only increases the tension between vampires, and eventually caged animals always turn on each another.

✦

OVERPOPULATION

Vampires are a unique species of animal, just as humans are. They must obey the laws of evolution as well as the dictates of their environment. They have a place in the food chain; indeed, one could even speculate that they fill an ecological niche. There are definite limits to how many of their kind can be supported in a given area. When they cross over the limit, natural phenomena reduce the vampiric population back within its limits, just as with any other predator.

Kindred are unique among the creatures of the world in that they are not held in check by any other species. They are their own prey and predators, and control their numbers through intense competition. The elders remember only too well that if their numbers grow too great they will attract the attention of the mortals. Although individual vampires are many times more powerful than their mortal prey, the sheer numbers of a humanity aware of their presence would quickly overwhelm them.

Only so many hunters can be supported by one herd. In years past only one Kindred lived within each city and each could claim it as her own domain. When cities were small, being a race of loners was an effective survival tactic. However, as cities have grown, so has the population of hunters. Now it is no longer rare for many to live within the same domain.

A large city, such as San Francisco or Hamburg, normally supports a vampire population of anywhere from 15 to 30 undead. Larger cities like New York or greater London hold a proportionately larger population, and fewer reside in smaller cities.

As a rule of thumb, assume that there is one vampire for every 100,000 mortals. Thus, the greater Chicago metropolitan area, a region of seven million mortals, can reasonably support nearly 70 vampires. Often a prince will artificially regulate how many Kindred reside within the city, thus ensuring the sanctity of the Masquerade.

Cities could certainly hold more Kindred, but there are legitimate fears of discovery. The Masquerade is the preeminent concern of the elders — better that some anarchs die than all be extinguished in another Inquisition. Every care is taken to insure that the existence of vampires is kept secret from the mortal population. Strict controls are kept over the creation of neonates, for a surplus of vampires dramatically increases the probability of discovery. The population is also restricted by the simple fact that few potential vampires survive their Becoming; many are driven mad by it and are put down by their sires.

Despite this, however, there are currently far too many Kindred for the mortal population to support; the ranks of the anarchs have swelled to unprecedented proportions. The time of the "grazing" approaches — the time fearfully whispered of in Kindred legend as Gehenna.

✦

NORMALITY

Most vampires desperately struggle to develop a semblance of normality in their lives and in so doing, escape the sordid truth of their existence. They create an artificial world around themselves, one that is bound to slip away with the passing of years, but is pleasurable for the here and now. Some scholars among the Kindred postulate that a vampire needs this facade of life to retain his sanity. Falling into the "vampire-schtick" of the cinema and literature inevitably results in despair and eventual mental disintegration, but for the duration of the play-pretend solace can be garnered.

It has been put forth by those with learning that much of the mortal psyche survives the Becoming. That psyche, however, becomes overburdened by the supernatural drives, desires and obsessions of the Beast. A certain amount of self-deception is necessary to retain one's sanity.

◆

SOCIAL
DISTINCTIONS

There are a number of different social castes among the Kindred. For the most part, Cainites are distinguished by a combination of age and generation (how many steps one is removed from Caine, the first vampire, in terms of ancestry). Although there is a degree of social mobility, the elders only trust those who have proven themselves, and the best way to prove oneself is to survive a few hundred years. The elders hold the power, so the elders determine who is accorded respect and status. Of course it is always possible to engage in diablerie and thereby lower one's generation, but such kinslayers are seldom welcomed among the elders.

The highest status is that accorded to the Antediluvians — Cainites of the third generation. The lowest is that accorded to the

childer and the clanless, who are generally of the 13th or later generations and have only recently been Embraced.

CAITIFF:

Even though many Caitiff are clanless but otherwise "normal" vampires, others have become so degenerate that they feed only off the weak and the dying. Some Caitiff live apart from vampire society on purpose, but many have been cast out. Some Caitiff were once a part of Kindred society, but have lost so much Humanity that they are unable to maintain relations with any other creatures. They know only survival, and live from night to night in search of food. Eventually they will die, but it may take many years.

CHILDE:

Vampires of this class have not yet been introduced to the prince, nor have they been released by their sires. They are not considered to be full members of vampire society and are thus shown no respect. They are, in short, treated as children. The term is sometimes used out of contempt. Kindred who have committed especially stupid acts may be called and considered childer.

NEONATE:

These vampires have been recently released and presented to the prince, though they have not yet made their mark in their society. The neonate is the caste of youngest vampires who have been released by their sires. If they behave themselves and do not join the anarchs, they will eventually become ancillæ, usually after 50 to 100 years.

ANARCH:

The anarchs have status because they are noticed and respected for what little power they have achieved. They are recognized for their energy, drive and consistency. Though they are the enemies of the elders and especially the prince, they are still respected, if not openly, for by rebelling they have given themselves an identity.

ANCILLA:

These Kindred are still young, but have proven themselves to the elders. The ancillæ are the up-and-coming Cainites, the ones who play by the rules (mostly) in order to achieve greater power. This is the rank between neonate and elder, wherein the vampire is given increasing respect and power. Most have existed for one or two centuries in their vampiric form.

ELDER:

When vampires reach a certain age, there are few above them who still hold power in vampire society. The elders are the Kindred who are in control and who seek to dominate all the others. The elders are normally between 200 and 1000 years old, but like all things undead, this can vary immensely. In Europe, a vampire has to be much older and more powerful to be considered an elder than she does in the New World.

METHUSELAH:

When a vampire reaches a particular age, somewhere between 1000 and 2000 immortal years, a profound change invariably overtakes him. It has long been argued whether this change is mystical, biological or is in fact a social change brought about through changing needs and desires. Certainly by the time a vampire reaches this age, a boredom and melancholy sets in, as well as an increased paranoia. Those who are weak, take risks or unconsciously desire suicide do not survive to this age — only the very strongest attain the station of Methuselah.

As a means of self-preservation, Methuselahs retreat from the world and those younger than them. The constant struggle of facing the young reckless ones, who seek power through the blood of their elders, grows numbing. Eventually one of the anarchs will get lucky and dispatch the ancient. Thus, the only option is to retreat fully from society and go into torpor. Some Methuselahs remain involved in power struggles and the Jyhad of the Kindred, but do so from complete anonymity.

ANTEDILUVIAN:

These are most ancient vampires, and they are likely the most powerful creatures in the world. For the most part they are considered to be the grandchilder of Caine, and are of the third generation. When they do involve themselves in the affairs of Kindred, they seldom leave things untarnished by their touch. The mere word of an Antediluvian is enough to provoke enormous strife and conflict among the Kindred. Their eternal struggle, the Jyhad, affects all the Kindred.

THE
PRINCE

The modern age (the last millennium by Kindred reckoning) has produced a new social order among the undead. At one time Cainites lived alone or with their broods; each was lord of its own city, and it is from that era that the Traditions came. Some gave themselves titles and honors, but this practice was unimportant as there were none but mortals to impress.

But when cities grew into metropolises, and there were enough vessels to support many Kindred, vampire society began to change. The age of the princes began.

The term prince, though sometimes used with contempt, is used to refer to the elder who holds domain over a specific metropolitan area. In formal terms, a prince holds the power of domain; he or she makes the laws and is responsible for keeping order. In practical terms, the prince is merely the one who is dominant and best able to keep the anarchs in their place. In the beginning, the strongest vampire in each city simply claimed domain. Over time, however, traditions have grown around the making and keeping of that claim. The Camarilla has codified and enforced these traditions.

After the Inquisition, the importance of the Masquerade was imprinted upon the minds of the elders, and they increasingly distrusted the younger vampires, whom they called anarchs. The revolt of the sect known as the Sabbat was the source of much of their distrust, for they feared that it could happen again. The neonates created during the 18th century were the children of a modern age, and alien to the mindset of the elders. After an incident in London in 1743 in which the Masquerade was broken by an anarch, the Camarilla decided to formally acknowledge what had already been fact for many centuries — the power of the prince.

The term "prince" is simply that: a term. It is not a titular holding, nor a hereditary position of any kind. In fact, many Kindred object to the use of the term "prince" for those very reasons. It is simply the name and the assumption of rights that a powerful vampire might achieve. Not all cities even have princes; indeed, some are ruled by councils, while others are not ruled at all. The modern usage of "prince" is a reference to the age when each Kindred was the secret ruler over the city in which she lived, a practice most common in medieval Italy. In some places, titles such as Duke, Baron or Count (in their culturally correct forms) are used.

The prince does not truly reign over a city; rather, the position is akin to that of an overseer. Above all else, the prince is the final arbiter of disputes between the Kindred in her city and is responsible for ensuring that the Masquerade is preserved. The elders generally interpret this to mean that the prince must suppress and persecute the anarchs.

The Kindred in the city owe the prince no oath of fealty and must obey only as much as their cowardice demands. When the rule of a prince is questioned or thwarted, the prince must use force to maintain control. If he does not have enough power, then his rule is at an end. There are some princes who do not understand the informality of their position; they believe themselves kings and their reigns involve much protocol and regal ritual. They hold court, and

demand that all Kindred within their domain attend them while they pass judgment on those brought before them. The arrogance of these princes is often more than can be tolerated, but it is understandable — who but the insane or the truly egotistical would want such a dangerous position?

Many Kindred ignore the prince, just as they ignore all others of their own kind. The powerful beings who together comprise the Inconnu, and many of the elders, are not impressed by such idle pronouncements of power. They see the title as representative of the arrogance of one still young enough to lust for power. The prince is not an authority to whom they would bow. When they visit a city, it is to them that the prince would bow, if the prince is wise.

✦

TAKING
CHARGE

The prince is traditionally the eldest of a city's Kindred, though this is no longer universal. The method of "coronation" varies from city to city and prince to prince. It is normally a violent usurpation of power, for only those with power and ambition are able to hold their claims unchallenged. Typically the support of the elders of the city is required. The most powerful of these elders are known as the primogen, and they often form a council of advisors to the prince. The prince needs their sanction in order to rule.

Anyone can make the claim of princedom, but only when none opposes the would-be prince may she hold domain over the city. If there is a challenge, the contenders must battle one another until sovereignty is determined.

This warfare is not as simple as a duel, or even any sort of direct combat. It is, like all conflicts between vampires, a part of the great Jyhad in that it is a progression of games and maneuvers, tricks and threats, violence and bloodshed. The various elders, broods and coteries ally themselves to one side or the other — either out of strong personal beliefs, promises of great reward or threats of retaliation. Frequently, mortal institutions that are under the control of a vampire, such as the police, banks or the media, may be employed in the war. Almost always, the process ends with the death of one combatant or the other. It is rare that the winner is magnanimous, and even if she were, the far-sighted primogen would not allow it.

Coups are difficult due to the fact that the prince is personally very powerful and nearly always creates a brood to protect him. Another consideration for a would-be insurgent is that taking on the prince usually means taking on the elders of the city. The elders, when united, have enough power to defeat all comers.

An attempt to usurp the princedom means a period of great instability, as the warfare can spill over into the mortal realm and threaten the Masquerade. Fear of this stays many elders from changing sides or dividing their support among two or more contenders.

Most elders support the prince because they do not wish to risk turmoil. They have grown protective of their long lives, and do all that they can to provide themselves with a stable environment. They are extremely conservative in all that they do, for they seek only to survive, not to promote change.

With the support of the primogen, it is nearly impossible to successfully challenge a prince, for these elders will direct their influence, followers and even personal powers to benefit the prince. Though many try to challenge the prince, most are destroyed before they even begin.

Thus, is it possible to rule the Damned. Princes have been known to voluntarily abdicate their positions, though this rarely occurs.

✦

ADVANTAGES
OF
PRINCEDOM

Many vampires seek the position of prince simply for the glory. There are, however, a number of advantages to the title which might not be readily apparent.

RIGHT TO PROGENY:

The prince is the only vampire who is able to freely create progeny. No others have this freedom unless the prince grants it to them. The prince thus maintains powerful control over other vampires, for most, at some point, wish to create childer.

PROTECTION OF THE ELDERS:

The primogen will generally support the prince as long as she maintains the Masquerade and suppresses the wilder stirrings of the anarchs.

POLITICAL POWER WITHIN THE CAMARILLA:

The prince has greatly increased status and is listened to by most elders.

MASTERY OVER THOSE WHO ENTER ONE'S DOMAIN:

It is the prince's traditional right to exert controls over all Kindred who enter his area of influence, and newcomers must report to the prince when they first arrive in the area. If they do not, it is considered within the prince's rights to punish them.

FREEDOM TO FEED:

The prince is also able to limit (for the good of the city) the feeding of others. In the name of protecting the Masquerade, she may place restrictions on some or all of the Kindred who live within the city. Usually this affects where and from whom they may feed. If they disobey, she may accuse them of violating the Masquerade and punish them accordingly.

POWER OVER ONE'S ENEMIES:

The prince has the authority to call a Blood Hunt, and thus possesses the power of life and death over those who cross him. He is not allowed to kill at will, but if the prince determines that any have broken the Traditions, he may punish them accordingly. This is subject to much abuse, and thus provides a great deal of power.

✦

INTRIGUE

The power-politics around the prince can be quite dynamic, especially when more than one elder is present and attempting to sway the decisions of the prince. Each may attempt to threaten, cajole and even trick the prince into doing things a certain way, all the while feigning disinterest in the whole sickly affair of politics. The elders do not dare push things to the point where the prince is overthrown, but they will play the game very close to the edge. The Jyhad exists on more than one level, and many different generations play the game.

By dwelling within a city overseen by a prince, a vampire must accept certain obligations. The city provides a certain security that all within benefit from, and to maintain that security, certain rules of behavior must be followed. In one form or another, most of these rules are nearly universal. They are known as the Six Traditions, and they are the oldest laws known to the Kindred — it is the prince who enforces them. Kindred relocating from San Francisco to Moscow can rightfully assume that these Traditions apply. Ignorance is no defense.

The anarchs rebel against all the strictures of the elders, their hated enemies, which are represented by the prince's power. These fledglings believe that there is little to fear in the modern world, and that the old superstitions and Traditions should be thrown away. Some believe that the Masquerade is but an embodiment of the terror of Kindred grown too old and too fearful. The prince must constantly work to keep the anarchs in line, and prevent them from creating any disruption in the Masquerade. Sometimes threats are not enough.

Most anarchs do not believe that Gehenna is a threat, and many doubt that the original vampire was Caine. They simply do not believe these legends, and treat them as they do the stories of a Garden of Eden or a Tower of Babel. They suspect that the elders use such stories to put fear into ancillæ and thereby control them all the better. Among the anarchs, it is considered bad form to admit to any faith in such myths. They chafe against the restrictions placed by the elders, and have not yet learned the wisdom of age. The fledglings are largely powerless within vampire society, so it is no great surprise that they rebel.

The modern age has wrought much change in the soul of humanity, and it is from these humans that new vampires are created. With the increasingly rapid changes in modern culture, many Kindred expect a wave of increasingly rebellious anarchs. Some within the Camarilla have called for a halt to the creation of new vampires, but it is unlikely that any sort of ban could ever be enforced. Most elders simply trust that natural factors will take their course and that the most radical of the anarchs will be wiped out before they can give the vampire community away.

✦

PRIMOGEN

Most princes are "advised" by a group of elders who are collectively known as the primogen. Collectively, these elders can be considered the most powerful Kindred in the city; individually, they either are not quite as powerful as the prince, or do not care to endanger or bore themselves with the duties of such.

The primogen is extremely influential, and serves as an important check on the dictatorial powers of the prince. At the same time, its members usually have their own agendas, and it is not uncommon for their bickering and infighting to cause as much trouble as any prince's high-handed commandments.

✦

ELYSIUM

A prince often declares certain portions of his domain to be free from the taint of violence. Such locations are known as the Elysium, and they tend to be the places where the elders of the city spend most of their time. Much intrigue and debate occurs at these locations, and it is in the Elysium that the business of the city takes place. Though on rare occasions the sanctity of the Elysium is violated, the *Pax Vampirica* is usually upheld.

Normally certain buildings are designated to be a part of the Elysium, most commonly places devoted to the fine arts or places which are in some way artistically or intellectually stimulating. Thus the Elysium tends to be in such places as the opera, theaters, art museums and art galleries. Sometimes the havens of certain Kindred or even nightclubs are so designated.

The rules for Elysium are typically quite simple. First and foremost, no violence is permitted on the premises against Kindred, kine or physical objects. On pain of Final Death no art is to be destroyed (thus making the Toreador among the strongest supporters of the custom of Elysium). Elysium is considered neutral ground, with no conflicts between Kindred allowed upon its premises. Thus, while intrigue and verbal sparring can be quite fierce, rarely does the

conflict escalate to violence. Finally, most consider it very bad
manners to attract attention entering or leaving Elysium. Some areas
are closed at night, and thus special arrangements have been made for
Kindred to leave and enter.

◆

THE
TRADITIONS

The Six Traditions form the age-old code of laws of the Kindred,
passed down from the early days following the kin-slaying that begat
the second cycle. The Traditions are not formal, written laws, but are
nevertheless known by all Kindred. There are many variations, and
though the words may vary, the intent endures.

It has become something of a ritual for the Traditions to be recited
by a sire to his progeny, just before presentation to the prince.
Though the fledgling may know of the Traditions already, the words
are still spoken. It is a vital element of the Becoming.

Some Kindred maintain that these codes were originally conceived
by Caine himself when he sired the second generation of Kindred.
Thus, it is possible that these words are those of the ancient one
himself, as he spoke them to his own progeny. However, it is far more
likely that the Traditions were created by the Antediluvians in their
attempt to restrict their own progeny. The tradition of the
Masquerade is likely to have existed for some time, though in much
more diluted form. It was not until the Inquisition that it was
reaffirmed and its wording and intent strengthened.

Many of the laws below are couched in fairly formal terms. These
are the words and phrases of the elders, and not necessarily how they

would be expressed by the anarchs. Many younger Kindred see the Traditions in an entirely different light.

✦

THE
TRADITION
OF
THE
MASQUERADE

The First Tradition is the heart of what has become known as the Masquerade. Age-old law demands that the knowledge of the existence of true vampires be kept from mortal humanity. To reveal such to them would place the Kindred in dire jeopardy.

Violation of this tradition is the most serious offense a vampire can commit. The strengths and resources of humanity in the modern age are such that were human and Kindred to war, the survival of the Kindred would be in question. In more superstitious times, this tradition was less revered.

To violate this tradition is to risk one's own destruction and the destruction of all the Kindred.

✦

THE
TRADITION
OF
DOMAIN

This tradition has faded in importance as the population of the cities has risen so dramatically. Individual vampires no longer claim

domain, but leave the rights of such to the prince.

Now, only the most powerful vampires in a city can claim domain over it. They do so according to the tradition, and pretend that all others live there only at the pleasure of the prince. Princes claim they possess the cities, and in most ways, they do. This tradition is used by them to support their claims. This tradition is what gives a vampire the right to claim princedom.

There is a prevalent misconception among anarchs that princes give different portions of their domains to favored associates as "turf." Though a prince only allows certain trusted Kindred to watch over portions of the city, this has only increased the cry for the rights of domain. Increasing numbers of Kindred are claiming "turf" within the city and treating it as their own private hunting grounds. Broods or even solitary Kindred stake claim to certain prime areas of the city (such as slum areas) and attempt to prevent other Kindred from feeding there. Though the city is vast enough that such claims have little value, they seem to have a special worth to these downtrodden anarchs. Few if any princes actually grant territory, but that is not enough to prevent the anarchs from taking it for themselves.

Some of the younger Kindred have made attempts to revive the tradition of domain, seeing in it a similarity to some of the mechanics of organized crime. Small gangs will often attempt to establish turf within a city, often in opposition to the other Kindred. This often becomes a difficult situation, with the fear of strife looming over everyone's heads. Because of this, gang problems within a city can easily endanger the Masquerade. If the gang supports the prince, its members may be tolerated, or they may have the power to resist all attempts to dislodge them. Elders do not like to confront gangs of anarchs. Though the elders possess superior power, there is still too much risk of death.

The anarchs primarily fight among themselves over turf, and usually do not attempt to prevent elders from feeding on their turf. Their activities are frowned upon by the prince, but as long as they do not threaten the Masquerade and do not get out of control, the anarchs are allowed to continue their battles. Indeed, many princes view it as a means of using the anarchs to suppress themselves, and will seek to provoke internecine conflict.

In cities where the prince does not have a firm grasp on power, certain elders may claim domain on areas within the city. Their power may be respected by other primogen, and they may be tolerated by the prince if they in turn support the prince. The establishment of one or more domains within a city can create powerful political dynamics, as those domains, intentionally or not, create rival power bases. In fact, occasionally a prince is only the first among a group of equals, the chairman of a committee of elders who each stake their own claim to a domain within the city.

Regardless of whether he has claimed domain or not, each Kindred is to some degree responsible for the area around his haven or the area which he frequents. Although the Kindred rarely involve themselves in mortal concerns, the affairs of the supernatural are another story. Kindred are expected to report details of strange events that occur in the vicinity of their territory to the prince.

✦

THE
TRADITION
OF
THE
PROGENY

Throughout most of vampiric history, the "elder" of this tradition was one's sire, though a looser interpretation has evolved in recent times. Many princes have stipulated that they are the elder referred to in this tradition and refuse all who dwell within their domain the right of creation without permission. They insist on their approval before any mortal is Embraced and often kill those who disobey. Most Kindred obey, but more out of fear than respect. In situations where a neonate has already been created, the prince may claim the individual as her own, may declare said neonate and her sire outcast, or may even put them both to death. The Camarilla officially supports the right of a prince to restrict the creation of new vampires, understanding that it is the only way to control the population of anarchs.

Those of the Old World, the Europeans, are even stricter on this point than the upstart Americans. One's own sire must be consulted, and if a prince has claimed domain over the area where one has one's haven, permission must be sought from her as well. No amount of tolerance is given to those who do not do so.

✦

THE
TRADITION
OF
THE
ACCOUNTING

One who sires a childe assumes responsibility for that childe's existence. If the childe is unable to endure the burden of its new existence, it is the sire's responsibility to take care of the matter. If the childe attempts to betray the Kindred and threaten the Masquerade, it is up to the sire to prevent it. While still a childe, under the direct care of one's sire, a vampire has no rights.

If a childe takes actions which threaten the security of other Kindred, they hold the sire responsible. The sire must carefully weigh the maturity of the childe he has spawned. He does not want to remain responsible for the childe forever (though extremely long childehoods are not unknown), but at the same time he does not want to release the childe before it is ready.

Long ago, release involved introducing the childe to one's own sire, but that has since changed; now, the sire introduces the childe to the prince in whose domain sire and childe dwell. Until that time, the prince is under no obligation, unless he chooses otherwise, to recognize the childe as one of the Blood. Unless the sire protects the childe, any may kill or feed from it.

Following the release, the childe-no-more is allowed to dwell in the city with full rights. This introduction process is similar to that of the Tradition of Hospitality mentioned below. If the prince does not accept the childe, it must leave and find some other city in which to live.

The release is a great rite of passage, for the sire no longer retains any responsibility for the childe. It is the activity of the childe-no-more that determines if he is accepted as a full member of the community and considered a neonate. If he continues to be rash and foolish, he remains a childe in the eyes of all. If he shows the wisdom his new existence demands, others will accord him the respect given to an "adult."

✦

THE
TRADITION
OF
HOSPITALITY

Though vampires are loath to travel (the risks are tremendous), they occasionally do. Ancient custom dictates that when entering a new domain, a city claimed by an elder, the newcomers must present themselves to the elder. This was so even before there were princes, in a time when there was only one Kindred in each city. It was simply a tradition of politeness; one knocks before entering.

The procedure varies in formality from location to location, and even from prince to prince. Some require formal presentation and the recital of one's lineage, such as it is known. Others are happy if simple contact is made with an underling. Those who do not bother to present themselves had better have the power to withstand the prince's anger.

The prince has the right to refuse acceptance in his domain to any he chooses. This rarely occurs, except when the newcomer has a poor reputation or many enemies. Even those who do not present themselves at all, but are later discovered, are not often chased from the city. They are roughly presented to the prince, shown their place, and released into the streets once again.

Over time, this tradition has become a primary means for the prince to maintain power, for it gives her the right to question all who enter her domain. She may not have the power to expel the more formidable interlopers, but her right to examine all is unquestioned.

Some Kindred bristle at the thought of having to "present" themselves for acceptance. Many are too proud and have a strong independent streak. The anarchs have too little respect for the Traditions, while the Methuselahs have too little respect for the princes. The Methuselahs see themselves as demigods towering above mortal and Kindred alike and needing to bow to none. To them, abasing oneself before another is unthinkable. They existed long before the princes ruled, and can see beyond all princes, knowing who pulls the strings.

Many Kindred never present themselves, choosing instead to live in darkest obscurity. They hide in the cold, quiet places and rarely venture forth. They are tolerated as long as they remain unobtrusive. The Nosferatu are the best at this, for their powers augment such activities. These reclusive Kindred are known as the *autarkis*, for they refuse to become a part of vampire society.

✦

THE
TRADITION
OF
DESTRUCTION

This tradition has caused more controversy than any other, and reinterpretations are continually raised. It seems to imply that the right of destruction is limited to one's own bloodline. Only the sire has the right to destroy his progeny.

However, the shift in meaning of the word "elder" has resulted in most princes claiming this right over all those who dwell within their domains. They claim that only they have the power of life and death, and for the most part this interpretation has been supported by the Camarilla. The veracity of this claim is the source of much of the conflict between many of the older and younger vampires.

Most princes strictly enforce their monopoly on the tradition of extinguishment. All others are forbidden to destroy other Kindred. If a vampire is ever caught in such an act of "murder," no punishment may be considered too severe. Often the perpetrator of such a deed will be destroyed herself. The prince will usually investigate the deaths of those who have been destroyed in order to find the killer. Of course, the higher the status of the destroyed vampire, the more thorough the search for his murderer will be.

Only in times of great strife do younger vampires dare slay each other, though the elders are said to do so all the time. A would-be kinslayer had best step carefully.

Most often, the prince enforces his right of destruction by calling a Blood Hunt, which is discussed below. Only if a prince openly calls a Blood Hunt is he allowed to slay one of the Kindred.

✦

LEXTALIONIS

The Traditions do not stand alone, for there is and always has been a system of punishment for those who transgress them. The system is simple: a vampire who breaks the rules is slain. Those who violate the Traditions and thereby anger the elders are hunted down and extinguished by all those who hear the call. This credo of "just retribution" is known formally as the Lextalionis, and more commonly as the Blood Hunt.

Tradition demands that the Lextalionis can only be called by the eldest Cainite in a city. In modern times, this individual is considered to be the prince. Other elders or even ancillæ could call for a Hunt, but most Kindred would not respond, for they risk the wrath of the prince in so doing. Normally, a prince will only call a Hunt over a breach of one of the Six Traditions. If a prince calls a Hunt purely for his own purposes, few will aid him in the it, and the prince will lose considerable status.

Assisting one upon whom the Hunt has been called is a serious insult to the prince. Betraying the offender is often the only recourse to having the Lextalionis called upon oneself as well. Sometimes a prince will be insulted if a particular Kindred does not participate in the Hunt. If the prince is powerful enough, and the crime great enough, he may have the authority to insist that all Kindred who live within the city participate.

Before the imagery becomes too ingrained, it should be pointed out that the Blood Hunt is not truly a formal hunt. The vampires do not gather in a convenient park with their packs of frothing hellhounds, and then set off across the city once the prince blows a horn. It is both more informal and more serious than that. The hunters spread out over the city and scour the streets for the individual whom they pursue, calling in others once they track the target down. In true Kindred tradition, it is a secretive and stealthy hunt. Mortals rarely realize anything is amiss; they usually notice only that it is a strange night, full of bizarre happenings. If the police are controlled by the prince or one of her minions, they will either be pulled back from the streets or mustered to assist in the search (without truly realizing for whom it is they search).

The Hunt can be viewed as a violent form of excommunication. Sometimes the subject is not killed, but is merely maimed and then released outside the perimeter of the city. The Kindred against whom the Hunt is called becomes *persona non grata*. Any who find the offender have the right, in the prince's name, to conduct summary justice upon the outcast. They may also partake of the offender's blood. This is why the youngest Kindred are often the most avid pursuers in the Hunt.

The Lextalionis is not called lightly. Most Kindred can count on one hand the number of Blood Hunts they have heard of, let alone participated in. The Camarilla reserves the right to an informal tribunal of sorts, most often after the fact. Evidence is presented to the Conclave for and against the offender, and the prince's decision is either ratified or dismissed. The prince who has his decision reversed suffers no formal punishment, but often loses considerable status.

Sometimes the offender survives the Hunt (perhaps under the protection of an enemy of the prince) and may actually plead his case. Often, the threat of the Conclave, and the beginning of its proceedings, are enough to dissuade a prince from calling a Hunt. Tradition dictates, however, that once a Blood Hunt has been called, it cannot be stopped.

An outcast may attempt to flee the city and find refuge elsewhere. Many princes will offer this alternative to the offender instead of calling the Hunt. Though the outcast may flee, the Hunt remains permanently in effect in that city, regardless of who ascends to power in the future.

The Hunt is usually the business of the Kindred of that city alone, and word of it rarely travels far. In some cases, however, the crimes of the outcast are so heinous that emissaries are sent to the princes of other cities so that a Hunt may be called there as well. The most famous example of this was the outcry in the aftermath of the Whitechapel, England slayings during the latter half of the 19th century. A Hunt was called against the offender throughout Europe and much of North America. The culprit, however (the self-proclaimed Lord Fianna), remains at large.

✦

SECTS

Over the past few centuries groups known as sects have appeared among Kindred society. Many ancients deride the existence and concept of sects as "*. . . modern foolishness. The blood is all that matters,*" but still the power and influence of these organizations grow.

Well over half of the Kindred in existence belong to one sect or another; the rest either maintain their independence or are attached exclusively to their bloodlines. The largest and most dominant sect is the Camarilla, though the smaller Sabbat contends with it on every front. Though the Inconnu claim they are not a sect, they appear to have some sort of organization and stay well clear of the other sects.

✦

CAMARILLA

The Camarilla is the largest single sect of vampires as well as the most open; theoretically any vampire may claim membership, regardless of lineage. In fact, the Camarilla assumes that all vampires are members — whether they want to be or not. The founders of the sect view it as the Great Society of undead, and take offense at any suggestion otherwise.

The Camarilla's primary concern is the maintenance and preservation of the Masquerade. The sect was organized in the 15th century in response to the growing influence of the Inquisition. Historically, there have been many attempts by the leaders of the Camarilla to assert more authority over other aspects of vampiric existence. Each time, the attempt has failed in a wave of bloodshed. The princes do not brook interference into what they consider to be their historical rights and privileges, nor do the Methuselahs desire a competitor who could thwart their aims. Therefore, the Camarilla remains a divided sect of only moderate influence. The elders who control it use it as yet another means to oppress and manipulate the anarchs.

It is thought that the Ventrue played a primary role in bringing together the seven founding clans of the Camarilla. Their efforts and imagination certainly lay behind its improbable origin. Though the Camarilla holds itself open to all bloodlines, those that choose to participate represent only slightly more than half of the known clans. Only seven of the 13 clans were among its founders, and only these clans regularly attend meetings of the Inner Circle. Individuals from other clans may be a part of the Camarilla, but no other clan as a whole is.

The Camarilla does not openly recognize the existence of the Antediluvians. Statements about them are publicly derided. As far as the Camarilla is concerned, they are but myths.

✦

CONCLAVES

Conclaves are important and potentially dangerous political events in the Camarilla. Open to any and all, they are the means by which the Camarilla functions as a sect. Much care is taken to insure the secrecy of the Conclave site before the meeting, as is care devoted to physical security while the meeting is in progress; an enemy of the Camarilla could take such an event as an opportunity for mass assassination. The Conclave may last anywhere from a few hours to many weeks.

Conclaves began as a ritual gathering in the first years of the Camarilla. The Conclave was a method used by the Camarilla (and its Justicars) to punish princes or to remove them from power. It was a means by which vampires expanded their authority and dethroned those rulers who opposed them. The Conclave has since evolved into a method used to handle all types of disputes that are beyond a prince's domain or control. In the past, Justicars were supposed to call Conclaves before they passed judgment on a Kindred and exacted punishment. Recently, though, some Justicars have been calling Conclaves after exacting justice rather than before. Nevertheless, Conclaves are still held regularly as a means by which all Kindred can be involved in the affairs of the Camarilla.

Conclaves can only be called by a Justicar (of which there are seven at any one time). They are generally meetings open for any and all Kindred to attend. However, great strides are taken to keep these meetings a secret from the Camarilla's enemies and, because of this, certain groups of anarchs might not be properly informed.

✦

FUNCTIONS
OF
A
CONCLAVE

Usually, Conclaves are only called when they are needed and are held in the geographic regions most concerned with the problems at hand. The primary function of the Conclave is to make recommendations on matters brought before it. Any Kindred may bring a matter before the Conclave, and most concern the adjudication of grievances between Kindred. Often complaints against princes are brought up at Conclaves, as are petitions by princes to deal especially harshly with the anarchs of a city. Any action that would be considered a breach of tradition must be discussed and agreed upon by a Conclave in order to avoid future punishment by a Justicar.

The Conclave interprets the Six Traditions and, in some instances, may even establish new ones. It may also call Blood Hunts, even against princes, who are otherwise safe from them. In times past, Conclaves have been convened for the sole purpose of removing princes from power. The Camarilla has always vigorously maintained its right to depose the rulers of cities.

During a Conclave any matter can be brought before the Assembly (which encompasses all Kindred who are in attendance). However, members of the Assembly only have the right to address the Conclave if supported by at least two members of the Assembly. While the main issue is what brought them together, many have their own secret agendas to pursue. A Conclave is a very dangerous time for a prince, for he holds no formal power at such meetings and is responsible for all violations of the Traditions in his city.

There is often something of a population explosion after a Conclave, as princes reward those who voted in their favor, allowing supporters to produce progeny. Many times an orgy of destruction counterbalances this growth as the losers pay the ultimate price.

✦

POSITIONS
OF
POWER

The Assembly is the group of Kindred that has gathered for the Conclave. They can be of any generation or clan and must have sworn loyalty only to the Camarilla, which is assumed if you have been presented to a Camarilla prince. All of the resources, connections, and influence of those in the Assembly are assumed to be at the disposal of the Conclave. A particular member may refuse his assistance if called upon, but risks losing status and invoking the wrath of the Justicar.

The Justicar (or Justicars) who calls the Conclave presides over it. She acts as judge and mediator throughout the duration of the meeting, voting only in case of a tie. It is the Justicar who determines who shall speak, when they shall speak, and for how long they shall speak (giving her a great deal of influence over the proceedings). The Justicar also has the right to disband and reconvene the Conclave. All of these functions can be overridden, on a case by case basis, by a majority of the Clan Elect.

The Council of Clan Elect is composed of one representative from each of the seven Camarilla clans. Each delegate is usually the eldest of her clan, but not always so. Each clan has a meeting to decide who will represent it. The Kindred with the most votes from her fellow clan members is the elected representative of that clan. The representatives are expected to act in the interests of their respective clan when they sit on the Conclave's Clan Elect council (however, this is not always the case).

A Conclave's Clan Elect can override some of a Justicar's authority with a majority vote. The Clan Elect can override the Justicar's decision to allow (or not allow) someone to speak with a majority vote. The Clan Elect has similar influence over a Justicar's decision to disband and reconvene a Conclave. Caution should be used when attempting to override decisions. Justicars do not appreciate having their authority challenged and may place pressure on a clan to replace its chosen representative.

✦

THE
VOTING
PROTOCOL

When a Conclave has reached a point where it is time to vote on an issue, every member of the assembly has a say in the matter, at least technically. The voting is done along clan lines, and therein lies the rub. All of the Kindred place their votes with their clan's Clan Elect representative (who often has assistants to compile these votes). The Clan Elect representative is then expected to vote as the majority his or her clan decides. Of course, this is not always the case, as a vote may be influenced by personal goals, Blood Bond, blackmail and bribery. However, if a representative does not vote in the interest of her clan, it is unlikely that she will have the support necessary to represent her clan again.

✦

INTRIGUE

Conclaves are potential sources for a tremendous amount of intrigue. Once a Conclave is convened, any issue can be brought before it. Furthermore, it is not unheard of for various clans to influence one another's voting or election process. It is the vote of the clan's representative, not the clan itself, that determines the outcome of a Conclave. As such, many sources attempt to influence a clan's representative. In some instances, even the Justicar tries to influence the outcome of the Conclave. Great care should be taken when electing a representative, which is why the eldest (and most powerful) are usually chosen for this purpose. Overall, a Conclave is a place where diplomacy is the mainstay, with intrigue and betrayal awaiting the unwary and unprepared.

✦

THE
ORDER
OF
PROCEEDINGS

I. OPENING THE CONCLAVE

The Justicar opens the Conclave by ritually sending a messenger to "Gather the Kindred," even though this has already been done. He then introduces himself, stating his name, title, clan and length of time that he has served as a Justicar. An address will usually be made in which the Justicar comments on the state of the city since the last

Conclave. Decorum requires him to recognize the prince and the primogen but otherwise no special treatment is given.

II. RITE OF DELEGATION

The Assembly is divided into clans. Each clan elects a representative for the Conclave's Council of Clan Elect, if it has not already done so. A formal vote is made, in public, if required. Each representative then assumes her position at a table in front of the Assembly and states her title (if any), name, clan and generation.

III. RECOGNITION OF THE ISSUES

The chamber is sealed for this portion of the Conclave. A castalian is then appointed by the Justicar to prevent anyone from leaving or entering (usually an Archon). It is here that the reasons for the Conclave are explored and detailed (sometimes the Justicar will reserve some especially dramatic accusations until after the chamber has been sealed). It is also at this point that any other issues can be brought before the Conclave by any recognized member of the Assembly.

IV. DELIBERATION OF THE ISSUES

The Conclave doors are often opened for this session. It is during this time that evidence and witnesses that may pertain to the issues at hand are gathered. The issues are dealt with in whatever order the Justicar desires.

V. RESOLUTION OF THE ISSUES

It is at this point that those involved with the issues make their

closing statements. The Assembly votes and the Clan Elect, in turn, place its votes. This is a sealed session.

VI. ENACTMENT OF THE JUDGMENTS

It is at this time that any punishments or judgments are meted out. Once justice has been done, the Justicar reviews the purpose of the Conclave and the decisions that the Conclave reached and orders that they be remembered by all who attend (nothing is ever written down as it is technically a violation of the Masquerade). The Justicar ends the Conclave with the ritual statement, "So has our voice spoken on this night."

✦

THE
ORDEALS

Decisions made by the Conclave may be challenged by undergoing an ordeal. This can be nearly any sort of exacting trial, mission or quest that is given by the Conclave to test the suspect. Such ordeals may last only a minute or may take many years; if not completed satisfactorily, the officiating Justicar is free to assign any penalty. If a crime is considered too great to allow the vampire to complete an ordeal, the offending Kindred may face a challenge by one of her accusers. The two antagonists battle one another in ritual combat. This may be a duel fought without weapons, but with each opponent blindfolded, or a contest in which each sucks the other's blood until one of the two is extinguished.

✦

THE
INNER
CIRCLE

Every 13 years there is a meeting of the elders of each clan and, not coincidentally, the founders of the sect. This is the true hub of the Camarilla. Compared to this assembly, all other Conclaves are but puppet shows. The Inner Circle always meets in Venice, just it has done for the past 500 years.

Each bloodline is allowed one representative to sit on the Inner Circle. Only this individual may vote, though all who attend may speak. The eldest member of each clan present casts the vote for that clan. It is a majority of age. This is the primary reason why the anarchs are so frustrated.

The primary function of the Inner Circle is to appoint the Justicars — the judges of the sect. One Justicar is chosen from each of the seven clans. They act of their own accord, but are required to take the decisions of the Inner Circle under consideration. By decree of the Inner Circle, Justicars hold the power to deal with members of the Camarilla who transgress the Traditions. The seven Justicars hold the true power in the Camarilla.

The appointment of a Justicar is a long, drawn-out political battle; while the major bloodlines would each like to select the representative of their choice, it is difficult to obtain the majority needed. The losers in the intrigue end up with a Justicar of young years or weak powers who will be ignored for 13 years. Thus, those finally appointed tend to be compromise candidates or chosen from the lower rungs of a line. Sometimes, even obscure Kindred are chosen by elders who believe they will be easy to manipulate once appointed.

✦

JUSTICARS

It is at first difficult to grasp the relationship of the Conclave and the Justicar. The Conclave is forbidden by tradition to pass any judgment directly upon any member of the Camarilla. This tradition limits the possibility of any abuse of power. The Assembly's only avenue of control lies in its judges, whom it appoints to pass sentence.

Justicars have the only true authority, which they hold over all the Camarilla, and indeed all Kindred, *except those who sit on the Inner Circle.* They have the ultimate decision-making and adjudication power over matters involving violations of the Six Traditions. No member of the Camarilla is considered above them in this area. If one of the Blood is found to have violated the Traditions, it is a Justicar who decides the punishment. There are no guidelines concerning the punishment; it is left to the discretion of each Justicar. Their decisions are often harsh. They are supposed to hold a Conclave each time they wish to pass judgment, but over the years the Justicars have assumed more and more power and no longer feel the need to do so. Justicars can call a Conclave at any time, either to confirm a ruling or to make a momentous decision that a Justicar does not care to make himself.

The decision or action of a Justicar can only be challenged by

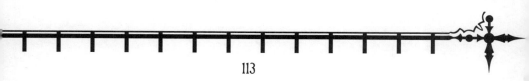

another Justicar. If a major point of contention arises between Justicars, a Conclave is held wherein the Justicars come together and resolve the dispute. The resolution usually comes in the form of a vote, but sometimes, depending on the dispute, personal challenges can arise.

Many elders resent the authority of the Justicars, and some among them are very outspoken in their opposition. Most accept it, however, for fear of opposing the Justicars, who are frequently of considerable age.

Justicars often have coteries of other vampires who do their bidding; these Kindred are known as Archons. These are often the brood of the Justicar and are always willingly Blood Bound to the Justicar. Archons enforce the Justicars' will and report breaches of the Traditions. The Archons are the eyes and ears of the Justicars.

✦

THE
SABBAT

Known to many as the Black Hand, the Sabbat is rumored to have evolved from a medieval death cult. Little of its nature has changed since then. It is the largest sect next to the Camarilla, and is aggressively attempting to increase its domain.

The Black Hand rules through fear, hatred, anger and physical violence. In North America, it holds undisputed control over Detroit, Toronto, Montreal, New York, Philadelphia, Pittsburgh and Portland, and is close to gaining supremacy in Boston and Baltimore. Until recently, Miami was also under Sabbat control, but recent events have caused a swing in the power balance there.

The Sabbat is organized in units known as "packs," members of which are strongly loyal to one another, feeding and traveling as one group. Indeed, in the Camarilla, it has become a derogatory term to call a coterie a "pack."

Members of the Sabbat come from many different bloodlines, though two clans dominate the organization: the Lasombra and Tzimisce. Though it may be possible to join the Sabbat, almost all members are created. The Black Hand requires strict devotion and adherence to the will of the group.

The Sabbat initiation procedure is designed to destroy any of the vestigial will in a new vampire. Initiates are slain, slowly and painfully, and then given the Blood. This blood doesn't come from one member of the Sabbat, but from as many as are present at the initiation, combined into a chalice. Once the Initiate has been given the Blood, he is buried alive and must crawl out in order to live. Those who do not spend eternity buried under the earth. The process of digging oneself from a grave tears the Initiate's humanity from him and opens him to the subjugation and brainwashing of the Sabbat.

Once the Initiate breaks free, he is Blood Bound to the pack that Embraced him. In a strange ritual, which occurs over two more nights, the Initiate is given more blood.

The Black Hand is concerned solely with power in all its forms. It is actively engaged in diablerie and has a fanatical opposition to life and its trappings. The Sabbat views mortals as lesser beasts to be dominated and used as need requires. The Sabbat worships at the places of the dead — cemeteries, tombs and charnel houses. The members of the Sabbat understand themselves to be undead, and behave accordingly. Any who oppose them are burnt; indeed, Sabbat packs seem to have a fascination with fire, though they are no more immune to it than any other vampires.

The members of the Sabbat revel in being vampires and living out their instincts. They consider the Camarilla's Kindred weak because the Cainites try so hard to retain their humanity. For the Sabbat, this is the greatest blasphemy.

The Sabbat often sends packs into cities held by the Camarilla, either to scout out the opposition or to hunt for those who have fled from the Black Hand's covens. Camarilla politics are invariably complicated by the presence of the Sabbat.

The Sabbat is said to engage in a strange sort of diablerie, wherein its members ritually butcher the elders of their kind so that stronger, more aggressive and younger vampires may take their place. However, like so much else spoken of among Kindred outside the Sabbat, this is unconfirmed. The princes of the major cities worldwide would give much to gain hard facts about the workings of the Sabbat. All of them fear the danger of its steady growth.

In the end, nothing certain can be said of the Sabbat. Indeed, all that the Camarilla believes about it could be false — rumor spread by Antediluvians who wish the two sects to fight. It is unlikely, but all too possible.

THE INCONNU

"Inconnu" is the term used to describe those vampires who have distanced themselves from the others of their kind. It is not so much a sect as it is a classification. The Inconnu are old, powerful, and as such have little need, and less desire, for the company of their brethren. They tend to live in the wild among the animals and sleep within the earth when the sun is in the sky. (It is unknown how they manage to live in peace with the shapechangers who rule the wild areas.) Certain Inconnu still live within the cities, and may even be interested in the Jyhad, but by the rules of their sect may they not become involved in it. Some have attended Camarilla Conclave meetings, creating great awe in the other Kindred. The Inconnu, like all Kindred, are always invited.

Most of the Inconnu have grown so old that they may sleep for months or years before awakening. They are like the Antediluvians in that they are no longer completely of this world, but have grown apart from it. Most of them are several millennia old and are the most powerful vampires that most Kindred will ever encounter.

Many of the Inconnu are members of the fourth and fifth generations who were at one point or another involved in the Jyhad. They have won their places in the hierarchy of Kindred by dint of age or through the devouring of their own elders. They have gone into hiding out of fear for their existence and out of distaste for the modern world. They believe that only by removing themselves from the world can they escape the Jyhad. Despite the best efforts of the sect, some of its members still become involved in the Jyhad. As a whole, the Inconnu punish all of their order who continue to take part in the Jyhad or meddle in the affairs of lesser Kindred. This is their only law.

A sizable minority of the Inconnu have actually achieved Golconda. This may explain their distaste for the Jyhad and their rational approach to many problems among the Kindred.

The Inconnu will allow no Kindred to harm or injure any of its members, no matter what those members have done. All rights to punishment are reserved solely for themselves, but it is very difficult to contact them to petition for such. In the end, the Inconnu are a most enigmatic and mysterious sect. Their organization and priorities are unknown, if indeed it can even be said that they have such.

✦

BLOODLINES

Many modern philosophers argue that the present age has caused an apathy and disinterest in the ties of faith, nation and blood. Certainly for the Kindred, the concerns of faith and nation are as dead as ever, but none care more dearly for the ties of blood.

While those of the Blood seem to be loners by nature and necessity, the need for society and structure seems to tug at them as strongly as it does mortals. This is most evident in the importance of lineage to the Kindred. Much of the respect one is due is based on the identity of one's sire, and the sire's sire, and so on. Even the most moronic of Kindred is entitled to some respect if his lineage is of regard.

At one time, each vampire could name her sire, and her sire's sire,

and so on all the way back to Caine. The importance of bloodlines has diminished of late, as Kindred have become more and more removed from Caine. Their connections to the elders of import are lessened by the many generations between them. The relative peace offered by the Camarilla has made them soft and self-satisfied, and they have lost respect for the elders. As might be expected, this is deeply resented by the conservative elders. Most Kindred created in this century know little of their lineage and seem to care even less.

Even so, within the world of the vampire the bloodright of one's clan is still of crucial consequence. Most vampires can trace their general lineage, if not the precise bloodline, back to an Antediluvian of the third generation. While the founder of the bloodline may no longer exist or may at least have dropped from sight, all of his progeny still hold many traits in common. Each clan possesses certain gifts and curses associated with it that others do not share; more importantly, members of the same clan hold similar values and virtues.

Represented within the Camarilla are seven major clans, though Kindred of any bloodline are welcome. There are allegedly 13 distinct clans, as well as innumerable minor bloodlines. Two of the clans are said to be of the Sabbat, while the remaining four clans owe allegiance to neither sect.

There are likely many more unknown bloodlines, especially when one considers the mysterious eastern Kindred, who undoubtedly have their own unique divisions.

BRUJAH

The Brujah are all rebels of one kind or another, forever searching for the ultimate expression of their individuality. They are punks, skinheads, bikers, rockers, freaks, socialists and anarchists. They tend to be stubborn and can be highly aggressive and ruthless. Sensitive to slights, they can be extremely vengeful, as well. They are the most uncontrollable of all Kindred.

These malcontents tend to be fanatical in their disparate beliefs — the only thing that unifies them is their desire to overthrow the social system, be it vampiric or mortal, and to replace it with one of their own making (or with nothing at all). Many are bullheaded crusaders of the worst sort: those who are so devoted to their causes that they are blind to any other shades of truth.

Though the Brujah are incredibly fractious, they come to each other's aid in times of need, regardless of past disputes and antagonisms. If the Brujah call is made, the others will respond, but the gathered host will be enraged if they think the call was unwarranted.

The clan is poorly organized and only occasionally holds informal meetings. Indeed, they rely on their chaotic behavior to gain the results they desire. The other Kindred allow them their eccentricities; what would get other Kindred extinguished is qualified by a remark, "Oh, a Brujah." Insolent outbursts and fevered ravings are to be expected from the Brujah. The other Kindred have simply learned to provide the Brujah the leeway that would be given to no other vampire.

GANGREL

The Gangrel are wanderers, rarely holding to one place for any real period of time. In this, they are very different from most Kindred, who find a haven and hold to it. There is no record of who the eldest in their line is, and there are no established leaders of the clan. On the whole, Gangrel are unconcerned with such things. They are known for being withdrawn, quiet and solemn. They certainly keep their cards close to their chest.

This is a lineage of survivors — vampires who are capable of making it on their own. They do not despise civilization or the society of their Kindred, they simply do not require it. They are known for their lack of concern about crossing the lands of the Lupines (shapechangers), for it is said they have friends among them.

Gangrel always pick their progeny-to-be very carefully, seeking those who are survivors and capable of existing on their own. Once they Embrace these mortals, passing the Curse to them, they abandon them, leaving them to make their way in the world. Though they may watch their progeny from a distance, sires rarely intervene. When they feel a childe is ready, they present themselves and teach the childe the true ways of the line.

The Gangrel are very capable transformers, which may explain their ability to cross wild areas unmolested. There are no reports of them being able to transform into anything other than wolves and bats, but there are old tales of a Gangrel elder being able to achieve a mist form. Perhaps because of this Protean Discipline, they often have features distinctly reminiscent of some animals. Each time they frenzy, the Gangrels gain another animal feature.

If the stories are to be believed, the Gypsies are the mortal descendants of the Antediluvian who stands at the head of the Gangrel line. They are under his protection, and any Kindred who harms or Embraces one of them will answer to him. Regardless of whether this is true or not, Kindred are loath to harm a Gypsy. Members of the Gangrel clan are expected, through long-standing clan tradition, to aid the Gypsies whenever necessary. It has been known for them to be aided by the Gypsies, as well. Certain members of the Gangrel clan have adopted much from the Gypsy culture, including their manner, aspects of their language, and in some instances their dress.

MALKAVIAN

The Malkavians are all insane. But from madness comes wisdom, and from wisdom comes power. The Malkavians are true creatures of chaos. However, the Malkavians are also known to be clowns and pranksters. As with all things connected with them, not everything makes sense.

This clan is known for its destructive and nihilistic membership. Malkavians have a reputation for being sadistic and holding weakly to the sanity they still retain. But, if truth be known, such Malkavians are a minority. The members of this clan regularly surprise the Kindred, for they do not seem insane. This is so common that many Kindred believe the Malkavians have an undeserved reputation. However, remember that sometimes the most normal-seeming people have the loosest grasp on reality.

There is a long tradition among the Malkavians of playing practical jokes upon both kin and kine. The shape and form that these "pranks" take can vary wildly and can range from harmless fun to the potentially terminal. The Malkavians, when they interact at all with one another, tend to award prestige to one another on the basis of these pranks. Many Malkavians have the solemn belief that the Jyhad is a joke created by the founder of their line.

The Malkavians are very choosy about whom they Embrace. Typically, only those on the edge of sanity are chosen. The members of this clan search long and hard for victims who has seen so much truth that they have descended into the pits of chaos and thus have unique perspectives on reality. However, if the progeny-to-be is sane, the sire will make the Embrace and Becoming as difficult as possible, seeking to drive the mortal mad in the process.

NOSFERATU

The Nosferatu are the least human in appearance of all the lineages. They look something like feral animals. Their scent and appearance is revolting — one could even say monstrous. They have long bulbous ears, a coarse-skinned skull covered with tufts of hair, and elongated faces covered with the most disgusting warts and lumps.

After a Nosferatu has been Embraced, he undergoes an exceptionally painful period of transformation. Over a period of weeks, he slowly shifts from his mortal to Nosferatu guise. In the beginning, the childe may revel in his new-found powers, but soon the pain and the changes begin. It is likely that the psychological trauma is more painful than the physical trauma.

Nosferatu only Embrace those mortals who are twisted in one way or another: emotionally, physically, spiritually or intellectually. They consider the Embrace to be too horrific to bestow on any worthwhile human being. With the change into a vampire, the Nosferatu hopes to somehow redeem the mortal, to give her a second chance. It is surprising how often it works. Underneath the grim exterior, the Nosferatu are practical and mostly sane.

It is said that they revel in being dirty and disgusting and do little to make themselves look better (though there is very little they could do). Despite this, they are cheerful amid their squalor, especially so when others are forced to enter their realms. They are known for being grumpy and lewd and cannot be trusted to maintain the standards of civilized society.

Though they travel through mortal society, thanks of their powers of Obfuscation, they are not able to interact with it. Therefore, they must live apart. The habits that grow up from such a lonely existence extend even to their interactions with other vampires. They avoid all contact, preferring their own solitary existence to the burdens of contact with others.

Though they may not interact with other vampires, Nosferatu do remain cognizant of the pulse of the city. They favor such tactics as listening to the conversations of other vampires from hiding places, and have even been known to sneak into a prince's haven to discover the elder's deepest secrets. If you wish to know of any information about the city or its immortal inhabitants, you need only speak with a Nosferatu.

The Nosferatu do stay in contact with one another and have developed a unique subculture among the Kindred. They play host to one another with the most elaborate politeness and gentility. They share their information among themselves and, as a result, are probably the best informed of the Kindred.

TOREADOR

The members of this clan are known for their hedonism, though that is a misinterpretation of what they truly are. They are indeed proud and regal Kindred, highly excitable with expensive tastes — but hedonism is going a bit too far. Artists are always so misunderstood.

The Toreador are known to be the most sophisticated of the clans. They are concerned with beauty in a way that no mortal can fathom. They use the rarefied senses and tastes given to them with the Embrace to become as consumed and impassioned as possible. Ideally, to a Toreador, nothing matters as much as beauty, though in many cases the search for beauty simply degenerates into a search for pleasure, and the Toreador becomes little more than a hedonist.

Like all true artists, they search for a truth beyond the existence they fear to be meaningless. It is that struggle for truth, and ultimately salvation, that has brought them to what they consider to be their mission: to protect the genius of the human race. Toreadors are truly in love with the vigor and passion of mortals and never tire of marveling at their creations.

The clan as a whole considers itself conservators of the greatest artists of any variety. They specifically search out those who they consider to be the most worthwhile and bring them into immortality, thus protecting their genius against the ravages of aging and death. Toreadors constantly search for new talent and spend a great deal of time deciding who to preserve and who to leave to fate. Among the Toreador are some of the greatest musicians and artists who have ever lived.

The greatest weakness of the Toreadors is their sensitivity to beauty. They so reflexively surround themselves with elegance and luxury that they sometimes lose sight of their goals and become concerned only with self-gratification — the reputation of the entire clan suffers from these individuals.

TREMERE

The members of this clan are dedicated and extremely well organized. Others, however, think of them as arcane and untrustworthy. They are aggressive, highly intellectual, manipulative, and they respect only those who struggle and persevere despite all odds. The Tremere believe that they must use the other clans in order to prosper. "Be friendly with them, let them think that we are one with them, but never forget that we serve our clan first and foremost. If you must use your friends in service of the clan, then you know that your time was not wasted."

Tremere are an odd lot, indeed. They claim to have once been wizards who voluntarily gave up their "art" for the powers and eternal life of the vampire. They have never named a founder, and some claim they have none, having discovered and harnessed mystical powers to achieve their state. Many of the elder Kindred discount this claim, considering it like those made by other so-called "magicians" of Europe who are almost uniformly deluded or schizophrenic.

The Tremere link to the substance of blood apparently runs deep, as they are rumored to be able to use blood in special ways to gain extraordinary powers. Some believe elder Tremere were actually practitioners of some ancient blood magic. They also believe the knowledge of those practices has been passed down from generation to generation, such that it is now viewed by the younger Tremere as natural and commonplace, and certainly not magic.

The leaders of this clan are based out of Vienna, though they have chantries on every continent of the world. A council of seven elders is said to control the entire clan from the Vienna chantry. From that locus, they maintain a tightly ordered, highly hierarchical group — one that allows no one outside the lineage to view their inner workings.

The younger members of clan Tremere are expected to obey their elders without question. But this is not as true as it once was. Tremere typically have immense love and loyalty for their clan, largely because they are Blood Bound by seven elders of the clan. They come to love the clan because of the love they feel for their masters. Though there are some rebels and anarchs from the Tremere line, it is likely they are posing as such on orders of the clan, as part of its long-term plots.

VENTRUE

Old-fashioned and tradition bound, Ventrue are sophisticated and genteel. They believe in good taste above all else and work hard at making their lives comfortable. They are most frequently the leaders in the Camarilla, though some avoid what they consider to be the crude and decadent office of prince. They are cautious, honorable, social and elegant Kindred.

The Ventrue fancy themselves a clan of the modern world and deny that they live in the past. This may be true of the most powerful members of the clan, but many are not able to give up the habits and manner of dress of the time when they were Embraced. The attitudes and beliefs they held as mortals are never forgotten by a Ventrue.

Ventrue are most often found among the upper crust of the mortal world, most mingling and fitting in quite well. Their sophistication stands them in good stead among the elite of mortal society, and it allows them to control many of the more powerful members of the city. Because of the relative ease in which most Ventrue travel among such company, they often have a monopoly on the political control of the city. If something goes wrong, it is often to them that the other Kindred turn for control.

There is a strong Ventrue tradition that any member of the line may find safe haven with any other member, and cannot be refused. Thus, many Ventrue aid their fellow clan members before the need arises for this tradition to be called upon. However, harboring a fugitive in your haven can have detrimental effects to one's welfare.

Ventrue are very proud of their leadership of vampiric society and will always insist that they were the founders of the Camarilla. They will do nearly anything to retain their grip on the politics of cities and the Camarilla, and are exceedingly protective of their reputations.

CAITIFF

Some Kindred do not have a clan at all, but are of bastard blood. This is sometimes because they were abandoned by their sires, or were Embraced by outcast vampires. A combination of a thinness of blood and a lack of social training has made them clanless. This is a fairly recent phenomenon, and thus they are disdained by many of the older Kindred. Though many Caitiff are considered to be pariahs or anarchs, not all of them are outcasts. Some are accepted among the Damned, but none have yet reached an age at which they have achieved any real power. Indeed, it seems as though the greatest explosion of the clanless has occurred in the last 50 years.

GENERATIONS

Kindred produce progeny, much as mortals do, and different generations exist among them in much the same manner. There exist more than 13 generations of Kindred, and the more distant a Kindred is from Caine, the first vampire, the weaker that Kindred is. Kindred are commonly identified by what generation they belong to.

It is important to understand that generation does not necessarily indicate age. A vampire of the 10th generation could be twice as old as a vampire of the sixth generation.

If vampires engage in the practice of diablerie, the slaying and drinking the blood of Kindred of earlier generations, they may raise their effective generations. For example, if an eighth generation vampire slays and drinks the remaining vitæ of a seventh generation vampire, her effective generation is now seventh, not eighth.

✦

CAINE

Tradition holds that Caine, the Biblical slayer of his brother Abel, is the Sire Of All Kindred. There is much controversy over this within the Kindred community, as there are none still existing who can claim with utter certainty to have met Caine. Certainly, those of the second generation would know, but they're not talking. Some of the third generation who yet exist claim to have met a being who may have been Caine, or simply a powerful Kindred of the second generation.

It is an unresolved question — a mystery of heritage.

✦

SECOND GENERATION

The existing translations of the *Book of Nod* place the number of second-generation Kindred at three. Caine in his sorrow created them to live with him in his great city of Enoch. Nothing is known about these three.

One can assume, based on the *Book of Nod*, that they were slain either during the Deluge or in the First War following the Flood. As one might expect, all those of age are reluctant to speak of their sires and the great strife that overcame them all. Undoubtedly, some know more than they are revealing.

Were any of the second generation still in existence today, they would be powerful beings: akin to demigods, perhaps.

✦

THIRD GENERATION

It is believed that seven members of the third generation exist, though the names of only two, Lucian and Mekhet, are widely known. In common argot, they are referred to as the Antediluvians, and they are the founders of the 13 vampire clans. All remain hidden, lost in the workings of the Jyhad, the war that has lasted nearly as long as recorded history. They continue their struggle, but now instead of openly warring on the battlefield, they use subterfuge, guile and outright deceit. Their primary activity seems to be tracing the activities of each other and thwarting whatever moves their opponents make.

These moves seem to range from things as petty as the acquisition of a piece of artwork or property, to grand schemes involving nations. Those of the third generation see themselves as manipulators and dominators, and are split between living within and without the mortal world. It is unclear if this reflects the origins of the Jyhad, or is just what it has degenerated into. There are other suspicions, based on the origins of the word *Jyhad*. Some among the third generation may indeed have reached Golconda and are attempting to assist others of their kind to attain that state. They must war with the other Ancients who do not wish this to come to pass.

Those of the third generation are powerful beings, with abilities and powers only guessed at by their lessers. Some say they comprise the last generation to have true mastery over the powers of life and death, and can only die the Final Death if they choose to or are slain by one of equal power. Is this, perhaps, the Jyhad? A maneuvering to see who shall be the last of his kind?

✦

FOURTH
AND
FIFTH
GENERATIONS

These vampires are known as the Methuselahs, for they are nearly as powerful and secretive as the Antediluvians. Those of the fourth and fifth generations are most often the pawns of choice in the Jyhad, as they may have political power among the other Kindred. As a result, their numbers have dwindled significantly with the actions of the Antediluvians. Few of this generation remain active, and many have become Inconnu out of fear of the Jyhad and diablerie. The Inner Circle of the Camarilla is said to be composed of members of the fourth generation. There are even rumors that the true purpose of the Camarilla is to blunt the efforts of the third generation to manipulate the younger generations.

Though the blood of Caine begins to dilute somewhat at this distance, those of the fourth generation are still extremely powerful.

✦

SIXTH,
SEVENTH
AND
EIGHTH
GENERATIONS

Vampires of these generations are powerful enough to think they can resist the workings of their elders, and so remain deeply involved in Kindred society. They control the Camarilla (at least they think so), comprise the majority of the princes, and are the primogen of many cities. Those who remain in positions of visibility tend to be important figures: leaders of clans or bloodlines, or princes of great cities. Most of the princes of European cities tend to be of sixth generation. Princes of American cities tend to be of seventh or eighth generation.

Interestingly, the members of the eighth generation seem to be the last Kindred viewed as "elders." Perhaps it is because the majority of them were created before the modern age, and that is evident in their manner and bearing.

✦

NINTH
AND
TENTH
GENERATIONS

Though they are sometimes called elders, these Kindred often associate themselves with members of the younger generations. Members of these generations are frequently called Ancillæ, though of course this is based on age more than generation. Most were

created in the modern era, and thus are somewhat alien in temperament to the older Kindred. In more ways than one, they bridge the gap between the anarchs and the elders.

✦

ELEVENTH,
TWELFTH,
AND
THIRTEENTH
GENERATIONS

The most recent generations of Kindred are often called neonates. They are still powerful creatures, but the special gifts of Caine's blood (the unique powers and abilities) are rarely found here. Born within recent memory, the Kindred of these generations are products of societies that have received the benefits of, and been victims of, rapid change.

✦

FOURTEENTH
AND
FIFTEENTH
GENERATIONS

There are exceedingly few Kindred of these generations, and none beyond. Indeed, those of 15th generation have failed to sire any progeny. Their blood is far too thin, and they are too removed from Caine to be able to pass on the Curse.

L *isten sweet Childe.*

And learn what you must soon face.

The streets the Vampire walks are the same streets the living walk. It is the Vampire that is the difference. It is the Vampire of whom you must be wary.

Vampire society is built upon the principle of power. Those who exert it the most forcefully can claim Domain over the city, and by controlling the cities, they can restrict the other Vampires who live there. Though a Vampire may claim Domain over a city, never can one become Prince if one's claim is challenged. Once challenged, only blood will settle the dispute. Thus, only the powerful seek Domain.

However, such power is of little meaning to the wisest Kindred. The desire for it is a human instinct, and over time the desire and respect for power should disappear. While there are certain rights that go with it, only those who have not left behind their human needs require it. No Vampires may Sire without the permission of their Prince, and until Neonates are presented to the Prince, their sins are the Sire's responsibility. When wrong is done, only the Prince may call a Blood Hunt. Finally, those who enter the Domain must present themselves to the Prince, though we of the Inconnu, of course, do not ever submit ourselves to them. These Princes may be Elders, but they are not our equals.

The largest Sect among the Kindred is the Camarilla, and it is to them you must go. They live within mortal society, as well as prey upon it. They still struggle to preserve the Masquerade, to keep the mortals from learning of us. The Camarilla is the foundation of the peace that exists between

most of our kind, and it supports the Prince who rules each city, for they are the only ones with the power to support the ancient Traditions.

The Sabbat are the great enemies of the Camarilla. This group of psychotic diabolists lives outside human society, but freely preys upon it. They play a most potent role in the Jyhad, though they are not under the complete control of the Ancients. All who venture to their cities do so at their own risk. The Sabbat inducts their Neonates by burying them alive. Only a few ever manage to crawl to the surface; the rest must wait within the ground for all eternity — screaming soundlessly in their forgotten graves. In North America, the Sabbat controls New York, Miami, Toronto, Montreal, Pittsburgh, Detroit, Portland and Philadelphia, as well as a number of smaller cities.

And finally there is the Inconnu, the most obscure of the sects. We are the Eldest of Elders, other than the Antediluvians, and have distanced ourselves from the other Kindred. We are ancient, powerful and have little need for the company of either humans or Kindred.

Though you must be wary of the witch-hunters, it is the other Vampires you should fear most. The Blood of some Elders has thinned and they can no longer survive on mortal Vitæ, but must instead feed upon other Vampires. Many of us create Broods so that we can feed from them, as we cannot be Blood Bound by our own Progeny.

That is why I created you....

CHAPTER FIVE
REBIRTH

✦

So you have come all this way, just to hear my dying words? You should know better than to listen to the rumblings of a sick, old man.

Ha, foolish one. You crave to understand your predicament? You seek to know what you have become? To be told the secrets of the undying race, the flesh eaters?

Very well, I shall tell you, not because I am afraid, but because it is my last wish to tell you these things. Listen closely, for I will not tell you of these things a second time.

You are cursed, know that first. You are cursed, and you are condemned. Nothing you ever do will change that, for it is you who are evil. Do not pity yourself; the Damned are not allowed such petty sentiments. Never again shall you feel the pleasure of a pure heart. When you die, you will learn of your punishment. You are a monster, and none among your kind has ever been able to control the Beast within. Neither shall you be able to resist it. I know this to be true. You need but look into your reflection to see that.

The vampire is the pinnacle of the food chain; they are the hunters of the hunters, the peak of performance. On this earth, there is not a more advanced creature, a more rarefied tool, a more efficient predator.

The life of the vampire is marked by the crossed swords of ecstasy and despair. Torn by their extremes, vampires are wondrous beasts, as often venerated as reviled. Beauty of form and action, deadly of intent and purpose.

Those of the blood are descended from one being, the mythical Caine. It is said that vampires are descended from the third mortal being to walk this world, who was the first one born to that state. If it is so, and a vampire can trace his blood back to Caine through less than 12 Generations, then that vampire is closer to God than we mortals can ever hope to be.

A disquieting thought, yes? Ironically, the Kindred see themselves as being closer to Hell than Heaven; forever damned to walk the earth until fate or circumstance brings them final rest. The imagery serves them well if they are indeed the children of Caine — cursed by God to wander the earth, deathless, as punishment for the slaying of Caine's worthy brother, Abel.

It is said that mankind itself is doomed by the original sin of Adam, who disobeyed God by his consumption of the fruit of the Tree of Knowledge. It is only through purity of action and deed that mankind may redeem himself and achieve perfection. It is irrelevant whether you believe in Adam and the Tree of Knowledge, for its truth holds strong regardless.

None of us are perfect beings, neither Kindred nor kine, and we do not live in a perfect world. That is virtually all that can be said for certain. It is our duty to improve the state of our existence and that of those around us, regardless of whether we believe an ultimate reward exists for our actions or not. We must all move from our imperfect beginnings to a greater perfection above us. We must work to carry those around us forward, as they will be as weak as us. You may view the struggle as a ladder, if you wish: each rung, each act of goodness, takes us one step closer to redemption.

Do not be alarmed. I did not call you here to discuss philosophy. Or theology. We are here to discuss Humanity. Mine and yours.

You laugh at my words; you believe evil to be an antiquated concept. Evil is all too real, you but have to meet it to know its name.

Evil cannot describe an individual, although it can describe the actions that those individuals do. Vampires are not creatures of pure evil, lacking even the tiniest shred of humanity. No creature lives in such a world of black and white, not even them. You cannot judge them so easily.

How do we define evil? No, no, have no fear, I will not tread that well-worn ground. Still, though, it is a worthy question to ponder.

There are some, many in fact, who believe quite strongly that there is real evil in the world. Many vampires believe they are it. They point to the fact that Caine's curse was, and remains, transferable. They argue that it is God's will that Caine's sin should curse the world the way Adam's did, but in a much more direct form. The vampire is the agent of that curse — the evil inherent in the world. A very real, very active evil.

This disturbs many, as you might imagine. It is one thing for there to be temptation in the world, and the acceptance of evil, therefore, being purely self-determined. It is another to believe that there are actual agents of that evil. Many vampires see themselves as mankind's torment. They revile in their role of evil incarnate. Why should they not? They are already damned.

Others believe in an inherent duality of existence. They point out that there can be no true damnation without the prospect of salvation. For without the latter, the former has no value. Without hope, there can be no despair. Without love, no hate, and so on.

If this is so, then salvation is always attainable, even for the worst of us.

The vampire may be damned from the moment of his creation, but that only means the ladder he must climb is taller. His road to salvation is longer and more treacherous, but his redemption is grander.

This is the path I chose long ago. But fate was more cruel than my desire. And now you see me as I am. I am condemned for eternity for what I have done, and if I say it was done out of need, it is no excuse. Evil still flows in my blood.

Golconda.

There are other words for it, of course, but that is the one the vampires most often use. The ones who are concerned with it, in any case.

What is it?

Golconda is either a place or a state of being, depending on whom you speak to. It is the point to which all of Caine's descendants aspire. It is the point were true redemption occurs — the point of absolute understanding. The point where forgiveness is possible.

Forgiveness?

Why, of Caine's, of course. I have been told that one of the later passages in the *Book Of Nod* says (we pass these things along verbally you know):

To rise from the darkness

To soar from the heights

To reveal the light inside

To forgive our Sire his sin

And thereby redeem our souls

That is our struggle

That is our test

We are the blessed

We are the damned

We are his Children

To forgive Caine his sin would redeem all of his line. All would be saved.

All.

Even those who do not seek to forgive Caine. Even those who haunt this world as evil incarnate.

And therein lies the rub.

From the beginning, there have been those who believed their roles as evil resplendent, divinely proscribed. They do not believe in forgiveness. They do not believe in redemption. They have no need for such things. They are the Damned.

Those who climb the ladder, who wage the struggle, have always been at odds with those who see darkness as their Domain. The Damned do not see a ladder to climb, they see only the walls of their pits.

What?

Good against evil? Light against darkness?

Hardly. Can the ignorant be evil? No, no, I will not lapse into this either. You may, if you wish, view it in this manner, but your misperception will hinder you. Not all who aspire to Golconda will attain it. They will fall short because of their imperfections — failings that seem as "evil" as anything the darkest mind could imagine. You forget that the vampire must kill to survive. The older he gets, the more powerful the being he must consume to live. Are these the warriors of light and goodness? Yes, you begin to understand.

The word Jyhad has come to be used for the conflict between the factions. Realize that there are more than two; it is not a binary proposition. There are fanatics and conservatives on both sides.

A simple gauge of a vampire's power is by its generation. How many generations is one from the legendary Caine, the Sire of all the Kindred? It is known that some of a vampire's power is passed down to its childe. With this in mind, it is easy to understand how and why the oldest Kindred, those closest to Caine, are the most powerful. Caine's Blood, as it has passed down through the generations, has become diluted with each making. The youngest of the Kindred are nothing compared to their ancestors.

They are still, however, powerful creatures, but the special gifts of Caine's Blood, the unique powers and abilities, are rarely found here. Born within recent memory, the Kindred of these generations are products of societies that have received the benefits of, and been victimized by, the rapid change.

A glimpse back at the last 100 to 200 years clearly shows the tremendous changes that have swept the world. Changes not only affecting the geo-political world, but the realms of philosophy, science, psychology, medicine, law and sociology. These are heady times for those whose near immortality allows them to live through, experience and ultimately outlive some of these changes.

Many of man's views and attitudes of the world have been reshaped or recast within the last quarter millennia. Science has answered or explained many of the fundamental mysteries of life and the cosmos, deepening at the same time the mysteries of the Kindred. Though some have tried, the same science that can reveal the atomic heart of the molecule, or the graceful curves of the DNA spiral, falls short of rationally explaining the immortal vampire.

Where does this leave the modern Kindred? In a world that values reason and fact above emotion and mystery, where do we stand? Are vampires creatures of this world or are they, in fact, the ill-begotten descendants of a man cursed by God? And if they are, what future do they have?

What future, indeed?

But I apologize. I had promised to speak of what it is to be a vampire, today. Here and now.

Pay attention.

Vampires' great Jyhad is simply their fight for dominance, the dominance of the pack. They have slaughtered all other rivals, and now they only have one another to combat. They joined together to slay their sires, for individually, each of the elders was far stronger than the younger ones; now vampires war among themselves.

Their contest is something of a ritual, an age-old ritual, you might say.

Those of the third generation, progeny of Caine, now hide somewhere, working their strings of power from the shadows. In their day, they ruled great nations and wielded power the likes of which those beneath them had never witnessed. When their power grew too great and they moved to dominate the world, Caine himself is said to have moved against them. All of his line are as damned as he, and the assumption of power would have been an insult to God's desire. Many were destroyed. Those who survived withdrew from mortal society to manipulate in secrecy. Much of what came after was done in an effort to prevent such an event from ever occurring again.

It is just after that time that one can find the origins of what is often referred to as the Jyhad. From seclusion and in secret, brother warred against brother. Mortals, men and women, the great civilizations of man, and the potent forces of nature were their tools. They struck at each other subtly, carefully, fearful of again bringing the wrath of Caine upon them.

I believe Jyhad does have some etymological connection to the Jihad with which you are more familiar. I know you are thinking that Jyhad does not truly mean "holy war," though it is in that context that it has been used most often in the modern day. The term Jihad actually means to pursue the cause of Islam to the utmost effort. Yes, that may involve warfare, but it does not need to.

I believe the original progeny of Caine used Jyhad in the context of utmost effort, not in the context of war. Each would do all he could to achieve Golconda and stop those who worked to damn the world. Each would seek a path out of the misery.

The Jyhad may have been the origin of the kinslaying. The *Book of Nod* speaks more of it, but I have not read it. Regardless, when the warfare became too intense, too extreme, Caine stepped in and slew those he could find. I'm sure the *Book of Nod* is more explicit as to why, but I can only guess. I believe Caine saw his progeny using their powers, in whatever manner, and believed it to be an affront to God. Caine's punishment was, after all, intended to be a curse. His children should not profit from his sin.

There are also those who believe that Caine was tormented by the fact that he did sire others. He believed God viewed that, too, as an affront and further denied him any hope of salvation. If Caine does still exist, he might not believe in Golconda.

Yes, I and others believe that Caine yet exists. We fear him still. We fear that he will emerge out of whatever hole he sleeps in, view what horrors his Kindred have loosed, and bring his wrath down upon us. Oh yes, vampires fear him.

Those who understand, at least.

Many of the current generations do not understand the concepts of the Jyhad, Golconda and the struggle. They see only a deterministic world and are blind to the true choices before them. The choices of right and wrong, of morality and immorality, and yes, even of good and evil. They hear the words spoken by their elders, but they do not understand. The proof is in their own form, but they are blind to it. Hopefully, you will understand.

Why do they not understand?

Their elders are afraid. Afraid to speak of the struggle and afraid of Caine. To them, the act of even speaking of Golconda would reduce its importance. It is something they both desire and fear. Is your tongue so pure that you may speak of the holiest of holies?

Do you see now why I risk so much by speaking and you listening?

As you know, as a vampire ages he sometimes grows spiritually tired and must rest. Sometimes it is the shear burden of his existence that forces him to ground. For others, it is fear. Fear of all I have mentioned before. The first children of Caine, those of the second generation, sleeping now, each for his or her own reason. The Jyhad has been passed on to their progeny, and their progeny's progeny. The third generation are said to be the masters of the game now, working their machinations from the darkest shadows in the subtlest of manners, and hoping to overcome their foes without disturbing their sleeping sires, or Caine himself.

Yes, I will grant, it does seem very archaic, but you must remember that a vampire is a beast of antiquity. Vampires live so long, they do not know how to measure their life spans. They outlive most they could call friend and witness the constant discovery and eventual abandonment of scores of precepts of science, theology and philosophy. To remain sane — and, I suspect, most of all to remain civil with each other — they have established Traditions and customs to structure certain aspects of their lives.

In the Dark Ages, while the elders hid, the anarchs fed off the sick and the dying, the ones who would not be of this world for much longer. They were scavengers more than they were hunters. Tales and superstitions grew up about their midnight wanderings. This is perhaps why the Inquisition arose.

But, with the coming of the new age, when anonymity was permitted and encouraged, they gave up such practices. They could travel about, strike out at victims and then depart. Assisting in this transformation of our lives was their increasing understanding of their powers. Though the young ones today have less potential power, they have a greater mastery of it in the beginning. For them, the path to power and survival is not as difficult. Perhaps that is why they do not value it as much, and why they scorn the contrivings of the Jyhad.

Much has been said of the Kindred and their ways. The Kindred as described, however, are uniquely Western in thought, appearance and action. There are others, creatures of the Eastern lands — of China, Indochina, Japan and other places — that are in some ways similar to the Kindred we know, but in many ways different.

Many theories abound as to the source of these differences. Some suggest that perhaps they are descended from a different sire, from some master other than Caine. Others put forth that they are different beings altogether, like the shapechangers. No one knows, and no one who has gone searching for the truth has ever returned.

That's right. Ever.

Whatever their true origin, it is apparent they have a stronger supernatural nature than the Kindred. Though certainly beyond the mortal plane, the Kindred are physical beings with physical limitations. The creatures of the East seem less so.

There is a fear, a great fear I've been told, among certain of the elders that they suspect those of the East to be ancient players in the Jyhad. They could be descended from the progeny of Caine who fled East to escape his wrath.

I do not know, but time may tell.

There, I have told you as much as I dare. There is more to be told, but that will have to wait for another time, another place. I have risked us both too greatly already.

But how eager you seem, how you desire to hear more.

Ah, of course, what am I?

I am cursed, and I am damned, though I am now mortal. I am but a pawn, nothing more.

I have lived an undeath for over two millennium, but only now have I found peace. Redemption at last.

These last 12 years have been ones of great beauty and pleasure. I have rediscovered my love for flavored ices, friendly smiles, the sun on my cheeks and, yes, love — mortal love. What a gift it has been! What a transformation!

I do not know how I was able to survive all those centuries. Yet, because of these last 12 years, it was worth every second of agony. If only Yoreador had not seen me that day, if only her teeth had never touched my neck.

But enough of an old man's muttered recollections.

Do you wish to hear more?

You seem agitated?

What is wrong?

Have you heard something?

Yes! Outside!

Wait! What are you…

End Transcript <<09:32:14>>

Copy to File XS-78092

Routing Order—

   Transmit priority AA3

   Director's Eyes Only

Reference 72-AG-156

Transcript Sealed by Order of the National Security Agency, Special Agent William Shepard, overseeing.

CHAPTER SIX
LEXICON

◆

T here exists among the Kindred a distinct *patois*, drawing on many tongues and giving new shades of meaning to certain mortal words. One can often tell what generation a vampire is by listening to the parlance that she employs. There is a sharp distinction between the words used by anarchs and those used by elders. Using the wrong word in the wrong circumstance is often considered a serious breach of etiquette.

✦

COMMON PARLANCE

These are the terms most commonly used among the Kindred.

ANARCH

A rebel among the Kindred, one with no respect for the elders. Most fledglings are automatically assumed to be anarchs by the elders, and are despised as products of the 20th century.

BARRENS, THE

The areas of a city that are devoid of life — graveyards, abandoned buildings and parks.

BECOMING, THE

The moment one becomes a vampire; the metamorphosis from mortal to Kindred. Also called *The Change*.

BOOK OF NOD

The "sacred" book of the Kindred, tracing the race's origins and early

history. It has never been published in its entirety, although fragments are known to exist in various languages.

BEAST, THE

The drives and urges which prompt a vampire to become entirely a monster, forsaking all Humanity. Vide *Man* infra.

BLOOD

The vampire's heritage. That which makes a vampire a vampire, or simply the actual blood of the vampire.

BLOOD KINDRED

The relationship between vampires of the same *lineage* and *clan*. The idea is much the same among mortals; only the means of transmission are different.

BLOOD OATH

The most potent bond which can exist between vampires; the receiving of blood in an acknowledgement of mastery. This grants a mystical power over the one who is bound. Vide *Blood Bond* infra.

BROOD

A group of vampires gathered around a leader (usually their sire). A brood may in time become a *clan* (qv).

CAITIFF

A vampire with no clan; frequently used in a derogatory fashion. To be clanless is not a virtue among the Kindred.

CAMARILLA, THE

A global sect of vampires in which all Kindred may hold membership. Its rule is far from absolute, and it serves as a debating chamber more than a government.

CHILDE

A derogatory term for a young, inexperienced or foolish vampire. The plural form is *Childer*.

CLAN

A group of vampires who share certain mystic and physical characteristics. Vide *lineage, bloodline*.

DIABLERIE

The cannibalistic behavior common among Kindred, involving the consumption of the blood of another vampire. The elders do so out of need, whereas the anarchs do so out of a desire for power.

DOMAIN

The fiefdom claimed by a vampire, most often a prince. Invariably a city.

ELDER

A vampire who is 300 years of age or older. Elders consider themselves the most powerful Kindred, and usually engage in their own Jyhad.

ELYSIUM

The name given for the places where the elders meet and gather, commonly operas, theaters or other public places of high culture.

EMBRACE, THE

The act of transforming a mortal into a vampire by draining the mortal's blood and replacing it with a small amount of the vampire's own blood.

FLEDGLING

A young, newly created vampire. Vide *Neonate, Whelp* .

GENERATION

The number of steps between a vampire and the mythical Caine. Caine's Get were the second generation, their brood the third, and so on.

GEHENNA

The end of the Third Cycle; the impending Armageddon when the Antediluvians shall awaken and devour all vampires.

GHOUL

A servant created by allowing a mortal to drink Kindred blood without the draining that would give rise to a *progeny*.

HAVEN

The home of a vampire or the place where it sleeps during the day.

HUNGER, THE

As with mortals and other animals, the drive to feed. For vampires, though, it is much more intense, and takes the place of every other drive, urge and pleasure.

INCONNU

A sect of vampires, mostly Methuselahs, who have removed themselves from both mortal and Kindred affairs. They claim that they have nothing to do with the Jyhad.

JYHAD, THE

The secret war being waged between the few surviving vampires of the third generation, using younger vampires as pawns. Also used to describe any sort of conflict or warfare between vampires.

KINDRED

A vampire. Many elders consider even this term to be vulgar, and prefer to use a more poetic word such as *Cainite*.

KISS

To take the blood of a mortal, or the act of taking blood in general.

LUPINE

A werewolf, the mortal enemy of the vampires.

LUSH

A vampire who habitually feeds upon prey under the influence of drink or drugs to share the experiences and sensations thereof. Vide *Head*.

LIFE, THE

A euphemistic term for mortal blood taken as sustenance. Many Kindred regard the term as affected and prissy.

MAN, THE

The element of humanity which remains in a vampire, and which strives against the base urgings of the *Beast* (qv).

MASQUERADE, THE

The effort begun after the end of the great wars to hide Kindred society from the mortal world. A policy reaffirmed after the time of the Inquisition.

PRINCE

A vampire who has established a claim to rulership over a city, and is able to support that claim *nil disputandum*. A prince often has a *brood* (qv) to aid him. The feminine form is still prince.

RIDDLE, THE

The essential dilemma of a vampire's existence — to prevent the occurrence of greater atrocities, one must commit evil deeds of a lesser nature. The proverb is: *Monsters we are lest monsters we become*.

ROGUE

A vampire who feeds upon other vampires, either out of need or perversion. Vide *Diablerie*.

SABBAT, THE

A sect of vampires controlling much of eastern North America. They are violent and bestial, reveling in needless cruelty.

SECT

General name for one of the three primary groups among the Kindred — the Camarilla, Sabbat and Inconnu.

SIRE

The parent-creator of a vampire, used both as the female and male form.

VESSEL

A potential or past source of blood, typically a human.

OLD
FORM

These are the words used by elders and other vampires of antiquity. Though these terms are rarely used by the newly created, they are still the fashionable vernacular among the more sophisticated Kindred. Elders may often be identified simply by the words they use.

AMARANTH

The act of drinking the blood of other Kindred. Vide *Diablerie*.

ANCILLA

An "adolescent" vampire; one who is no longer a neonate, but is not an elder either.

ANTEDILUVIAN

One of the eldest Kindred, a member of the third generation. A warlord of the Jyhad.

ARCHON

A powerful vampire who wanders from city to city, usually serving a Justicar. Archons are frequently used to track down Kindred who have fled a city.

AUTARKIS

A vampire who refuses to be a part of Kindred society, and does not recognize the domain of a prince.

CAINITE

A vampire. Vide *Kindred.*

CANAILLE

The mortal herd, especially that element of it which is the most unsavory and lacking in culture (whom the Kindred largely feed upon).

CAUCHEMAR

A vampire who feeds only on sleeping victims and prevents their awakening.

CUNCTATOR

A vampire who avoids killing by drinking shallowly and taking too little blood to kill the prey; *faut plus chasser, peut mieux dormir.* Compare *Casanova* .

BOOK OF THE
KINDRED

COTERIE

A group of Kindred who protect and support one another against all outsiders. Vide *Brood*.

CONSANGUINEUS

One of the same lineage (usually a younger member).

FOOTPAD

One who feeds off the derelicts and the homeless, and who typically does not have a haven of her own. Vide *Alleycat*.

GENTRY

A Kindred who hunts the nightclubs, districts of ill repute and other places of entertainment where mortals seek to pair off. Vide *Rake*.

GOLCONDA

The state of being to which many vampires aspire, in which a balance is found between opposing urges and scruples. The slide into bestiality is halted, and the individual reaches a kind of stasis. Like the mortals' Nirvana, it is often spoken of, but seldom achieved.

HUMANITAS

The degree to which a Kindred still retains some humanity.

KINE

A contemptuous term for mortals, often used in opposition to *Kindred*. The expression *Kindred and kine* means "all the world."

LEECH

A human who drinks a vampire's blood, yet retains free will. Often, he keeps the vampire as a prisoner or offers great rewards for the blood.

LEXTALIONIS

The code of the Kindred, allegedly created by Caine. It suggests biblical justice — an eye for an eye, a tooth for a tooth. Vide *Traditions*.

LINEAGE

The bloodline of a vampire, traced by Embrace.

METHUSELAH

An elder who no longer lives among the other Kindred. Many Methuselahs belong to the *Inconnu*.

NEONATE

A young, newly created Kindred. Vide *Fledgling, Whelp*.

OSIRIS

A vampire who surrounds himself with mortal or ghoul followers in a cult or coven to better obtain sustenance. The practice is less common than it once was.

PAPILLON

The red-light district; the area of the city made up of nightclubs, gambling houses and brothels. The prime hunting ground of the city.

PROGENY

A collective term for all the vampires created by one sire. Less formal, and less flattering, is *Get*.

PRAXIS

The right of princes to rule, as well as the rules, laws and customs enforced by a particular prince.

PRIMOGEN

The leaders in a city or the ruling council of elders. Those who support the prince and make her rule possible.

REGNANT

One who has a Blood Bond over another Kindred, through giving said Kindred blood three times. Vide *Blood Bond*.

RETAINERS

Humans who serve a vampire master. They are generally either ghouls or mentally dominated by their vampire master. This control is sometimes so complete that the mortals are unable to take any action of their own volition.

SIREN

A vampire who seduces mortals, but does not kill them and takes only a little blood after putting the mortal into a deep sleep. Vide *Tease*.

SUSPIRE

The dream dance during the final stage of the quest for Golconda.

THIRD MORTAL

Caine, the progenitor of all vampires, according to the *Book of Nod* (qv).

THRALL

A vampire who is held under a *Blood Bond*, and thus under the control of another Kindred.

VITÆ

Blood.

WASSAIL

The final release and the last frenzy. Wassail occurs when the last vestiges of Humanity are lost and a vampire plunges into madness.

WHELP

A contemptuous term for any young vampire; originally used only in reference to one's own progeny.

WIGHT

Human, mortal.

WITCH-HUNTER

A human who searches for vampires in order to kill them.

WHIG

Name for a Cainite who possesses an obsessive interest in mortal fashion and current events.

✦

VULGAR
ARGOT

These are the words used most frequently by anarchs, the younger vampires who disdain and/or ignore the traditions of the elders. They seek to establish their own culture, and inventing their own slang is part of the process. Of course, they will use Old Form when they do not have another word for the same thing, and some elders have even begun to use the vulgar forms so as to create a greater effect when they speak.

ALLEYCAT

A vampire who does not have a haven of any kind, but instead resides in a different place each night. Also used to refer to those Kindred who feed off the homeless and other street people.

BANKING

The practice, most widespread among younger Kindred, of taking blood from blood banks. Chilled blood so long removed from the body is less satisfying, but some neonates delight in entering blood banks

and drinking to excess. This is seen by many princes as a breach of the Masquerade.

BANKER

A Kindred who engages in the practice of Banking.

BLACK HAND

A sect that involves itself in diablerie. Vide *Sabbat*.

BLISTER

A vampire who contracts an infectious disease, and subsequently spreads it to each donor from whom she feeds.

BLOODLINE

The vampire's heritage. Vide *Lineage*.

BLOOD BOND

A mystic servitude to another vampire as a result of taking the *Blood Oath*. Vide *Regnant*.

BLOOD DOLL

A Kindred who is held in Regnant by another. The doll is Blood Bound and no longer free.

BUTTERFLY

One who mingles among the high society of mortals, and only feeds upon the wealthy and famous.

CASANOVA

A vampire who delights in seducing mortals but not killing them, and who takes only a little blood, erasing the victim's memory of the event when she is finished. There are rumors that the original Casanova was or is a vampire, but this is not generally believed. Vide *Cauchemar*.

CHANGE, THE

The moment and the process of becoming a vampire. Vide *Becoming*.

DAMNED, THE

The immortal, undead race. All the vampires as a whole.

DONOR

A potential or past source of blood, typically a human.

FARMER

A derogatory term for a vampire who keeps animals for the purpose of feeding the Hunger. Vide *Vegetary*.

FIEF

A sarcastic term for the domain of a clan or prince.

HEAD

A vampire who feeds upon those under the influence of drugs, so as to feel the effects. The term *Head* is used with a suitable prefix if the vampire prefers a particular drug. Vide *Lush*.

HEADHUNTER

An elder who hunts other Kindred for their blood. Vide *Rogue*, *Diablerie*.

LICK

A vampire. Vide *Kindred*.

RACK, THE

The hunting ground represented by nightclubs, bars and other places of entertainment where mortals seek to dance, drink and pair off.

RAKE

One who habitually uses the *Rack* is a *Rake* in Vulgar argot; *Papillon* and *Gentry* are progressively older terms for the same.

SANDMAN

A vampire who feeds only upon sleeping victims. Vide *Cauchemar*.

SLUMMING

The act of feeding from the homeless and derelicts. A vampire who does so exclusively is a *Slummer*.

STALKER

A mortal who hunts the Kindred. Vide *Witch-hunter*.

TEASE

A term sometimes used for a female *Casanova* (qv).

TURF

The city or section of a city that vampires might try to claim for themselves. Vide *Fief, domain*.

VEGETARY

A sarcastic term for a vampire who refuses to take the blood of humans, but relies instead on that of animals. Vide *Farmer*.

CHAPTER SEVEN
EYE OF THE BEHOLDER

✦

LAWRENCE WATT-EVANS

Bethany felt the warm blood welling up and filling her mouth, felt the hot frenzy of the Hunger — but she wasn't seeing the hapless drunkard she had settled on for her latest meal.

She saw Anton.

Anton Prihar, dangling there in his studio, the thick, ugly noose tight around his throat. Anton Prihar, who had died rather than let her Embrace him and turn him into one of the Kindred. Anton, who had loved the sun's light so much that he had refused an offer of eternal life, because it meant giving up the day.

She closed her eyes, and she still saw him, hanging surrounded by his paintings, twisting slowly, his face congested and swollen.

How could he *do* that?

How could he do that to *her*?

She swallowed mechanically and let the blood fill her, strengthen her.

She would need her strength if she truly meant to do what she had promised herself she would do. She just hoped that the strength of the blood would be enough.

Sated at last, she rose from her kill, the image of Anton faded for the moment. Flush with power, she saw the world around her in awesome clarity, in sharp-edged precision. The brick wall beside her was rich with textures, the air of the alley thick with scents, the sky above her awash in subtle color. For once, there was no morning fog.

A man at the mouth of the alley was looking at her — she could see him, smell him, hear his heartbeat and his shallow breath. He didn't seem to have noticed her victim, or if he had, he hadn't understood what was happening. Bethany smiled disarmingly at him, and took a step nearer, to where she could see that one of his eyes, the left, was so bloodshot as to appear almost solid red.

Then the man turned and walked away, as if nothing had happened.

Bethany frowned as she realized that the man had seen her, been aware of her, and hadn't cared. He had dismissed her as unimportant, irrelevant — but how could he? She was one of the Kindred and a Toreador, at the height of her power; he should have been fascinated by her.

It didn't matter, though. Ordinarily she might have pursued him, made sure that he wouldn't do anything to damage the Masquerade, but not tonight. Tonight she had other concerns.

The sky above her was beginning to lighten; the time was coming. She leapt up and caught the lowest rung of the fire escape above her, then pulled herself quickly upward.

A moment later she was on the roof, staring eastward, out across the bay to where the sky above the Oakland hills was turning pale and pink.

To her heightened senses the colors were magnificent. Was this what Anton had seen that had so captivated him?

But mere kine couldn't see as clearly as she did, she knew that. Anton had had a true artist's perceptions, but he had been merely human, after all; he could not have seen with a vampire's eye.

Was there perhaps something Anton had seen in the sunlight that a vampire could not?

Bethany had been human once, forty years earlier; she tried to remember what it was like, whether there was something that she had lost in the Embrace, when she had gained so much. There had been certain immature feelings that she had shed, a foolish warmth and naive compassion that she had cast aside, but she could not recall any lessening of any kind in her experience of the physical world.

No, whatever Anton had seen in the sunlight was not a matter of his eye seeing more than hers could.

But he had seen *something*.

The first rays of dawn burst upward, painting gold across the sky, and she stared.

It was beautiful, there was no question of that, it was intensely beautiful… but she could feel the sun's heat on her face, even though the air was still cool. It stung her skin, it almost burned — and the sun's disk had yet to actually cross the horizon.

It was painful, yes, but she had survived plenty of pain in her life. Mere physical pain was far easier to bear than much of what had happened to her, back when she was young, both before and after the Embrace.

There were many among the Kindred who would say she was still young, young and foolish, but she knew she had learned much. She had learned to endure through pain. She had even learned to appreciate the beauty of the pain itself.

Golden light flared as the sun itself appeared, and the light cut at her like knives; she remembered Anton's painting where knife-edged sunlight had cut down the city streets. Had he somehow felt this the way she did?

She could feel her skin burning and reddening, but she stared in fascination as the sunlight transformed the sky and the landscape. The colors were so *different*, so *vivid* — she had forgotten, after forty years of darkness, how bright the sun was. The rich blue and shining gold of the sky seemed to burn into her....

And she knew that they *were* burning her; the pain was exquisite.

At last the pain grew unbearable and irresistible, overwhelming the fascination, and she knew that if she stayed any longer she would be risking her very existence. She forced herself to move, to grab the railing with blistered hands and climb down the fire escape on throbbing feet, her eyes almost blind in the shadows after looking into the glory of the sunrise. Wounded, limping, she made her way to the shelter she had prepared.

Oddly, she thought as she climbed, it had taken a greater force of will to tear herself away from the light and pain than it had taken to confront it in the first place.

And as she went, she remembered the transcendent beauty of the dawn — the beauty that she shared with Anton, the beauty the rest of the Kindred had forsaken.

That was worth any pain.

✦

"She has no protector," Allanyan Serata said, as she toyed with the medallion she wore. "Her Sire is gone, her grandSire will not risk his studied neutrality on her behalf, and the Prince owes her no special favor."

"I am aware of that," Stefan said dryly. He was not so much standing before Serata's throne as slouching there, with the casual insouciance he had made a part of himself.

"And you didn't see fit to tell me?" Serata demanded.

"You didn't see fit to ask me," Stefan retorted.

Serata stared coldly at him, and Stefan realized he had overstepped. He straightened and bowed slightly; a chain jingled. "My apologies," he said. "I had not realized you were so concerned."

"I am the Primogen of the clan for this city," Serata replied. "This upstart Artiste has cost me a precious resource; am I to simply tolerate that? If I allow this once, will I be able to prevent other, similar discourtesies in the future? No, any sort of defiance of my will must be punished, swiftly and forcefully."

"I see that," Stefan conceded.

"And as my faithful servant — and you *are* my faithful servant, are you not, dear Stefan? As my faithful servant, was it not your place to anticipate my desire to punish this Bethany? Was it not your duty to discover for me whatever difficulties there might be in administering this punishment, and to inform me of those difficulties — or of their absence? Was it wise to leave it to me, acting on my own, to determine that this neonate is defenseless?"

Stefan bowed his head again. "I rely on *your* wisdom, madame, for clearly my own is lacking."

Serata's lips twisted sardonically. "And what of your ingenuity, Stefan? Is that in any better condition?"

Stefan smiled back. "I would like to think that it is, madame, but I have had little cause to put it to the test of late."

"Well, then, little one, here's your opportunity. I do not wish this Bethany destroyed outright — allowing a human artist's suicide would not justify so extreme a response, even in this case, and I do not care to excessively alienate others of her faction, as many of the Artistes have the Prince's ear. Rather, I'd have *you* devise a suitable penalty for her. Consider this to be your penance for your own part in allowing Anton Prihar to slip through our fingers — that you shall arrange and carry out an appropriate vengeance against Bethany. Do you think you can come up with some artistic response to her affront?"

"Of course," Stefan replied, trying not to show any discomfort. "It should be a delightful challenge."

"Good," Serata said, sitting back on her velvet throne. "See to it, then."

✦

The first step, of course, was to locate Bethany.

Vampires survive through invisibility, through going unseen even in the midst of the cities built by their prey. The Kindred's senses are far greater than those of kine, and a vampire's knowledge of vampiric ways is necessarily far greater, but still, finding a single specific vampire who does not wish to be found is not always an easy task, even for one of the Kindred.

Stefan had to admit to himself that he was not particularly enthusiastic about finding Bethany; she hated him for his part in that artist's death, and he did not enjoy being hated for something he had

not meant to do. Still, he had been ordered to do so, and he had to at least make an effort.

And it would be best to find her quickly and get it over with.

He began his search at the Vampire Club, the gathering place and neutral ground for their kind. He moved from one airless underground room to the next, greeting those he recognized among the patrons, asking those he knew well whether they had seen Bethany of late. No one admitted having encountered her recently.

He did no better in the above-ground Alexandrian Club.

Stefan began to worry at that; what if Bethany had fled the city? Serata might insist he go after her. He did not relish the prospect of pursuing her to the ends of the earth; such a hunt could take years and might take him to places where the local powers would frown on any sort of artistic revenge.

Another possibility was that Bethany had been destroyed. That might be even worse; how would Serata take being cheated of her vengeance? She might simply accept it as the workings of Fate, but she might equally well decide to take out her frustration on Stefan.

He wished he had not tied his own prospects quite so closely to Serata' s.

Stefan remained in the Alexandrian Club for hours, watching Kindred and kine pass in and out, hoping to spot Bethany, or to find someone who knew of her whereabouts.

His hopes waned steadily as the night wore on, but at last, as he was about to leave, he tried one final question of a new arrival.

"I haven't seen her lately," the vampire replied. "I heard that she's been hunting the area between the Embarcadero and Telegraph Hill, though."

That was more than Stefan had gotten elsewhere, and at least she was still in the city. He thanked the man and hurried out the door.

Once outside, though, he saw that the eastern sky was beginning to go pale; there wasn't time to track her down before dawn.

The following night Stefan set out patrolling the streets, block by block.

It wasn't until three nights later, not long before dawn, that he spotted a thin woman in black climbing a fire escape. He could see no details at such a distance, but it certainly *could* have been Bethany.

A fire escape — what would she be doing there? Had Bethany resorted to breaking into apartments at random? That hardly seemed likely; she had never had any difficulty in finding her prey through more traditional, more entertaining methods. She had been a lovely young woman when Embraced, and forty years later her beauty was untouched — if anything, it had been heightened by her vampiric pallor and grace. Stefan could not imagine that she would ever have any difficulty in finding men who would accompany her to private places.

He turned down the alley and almost tripped over the corpse she had left.

A glance and the smell told him immediately that yes, this was a vampire's kill. Unforgivably sloppy, he thought, to leave it here like this! He looked up. The woman in black had reached the top of the fire escape and was climbing onto the roof.

That was interesting; then she wasn't breaking in windows. But what *did* she want up there?

Was it really Bethany?

He jumped and caught the fire escape and began climbing. On the final ladder, his head still a foot or so below the coaming, he hesitated — what if this was some sort of trap? What if he was walking into a diabolist's lair?

"Bethany?" he called.

No one answered.

"Bethany?" he called again, more loudly.

"Anton?"

The answer was unexpected, but it was Bethany's voice. Stefan heaved himself upward, onto the roof.

"No," he said, "it's I, Stefan."

She was sitting cross-legged in the center of the roof, staring east, away from him.

"Go away, Stefan," she said, without looking at him.

Though the words were unwelcoming, the voice was not as hate-filled as he had expected; she sounded almost resigned. He took a wary step toward her. He had been so concerned with finding her, he realized, that he had given no thought to just what sort of suitably artistic revenge he might take on her. Her asking if he was Anton, though — that might provide possibilities. Did she think someone had found a way to revive Anton Prihar? She should know better. Was there another Anton, perhaps? He regretted giving his correct name; he should have claimed to have been Anton, he thought.

"Bethany?" he said. "What are you doing here? I've been looking all over the city for you."

"Whatever for?" She still didn't turn to face him; she was staring fixedly at the Oakland hills, across the bay.

She clearly didn't want to talk to him — but on the other hand, she wasn't afraid of him, either, or she would be watching him. Perhaps, he thought, if he could gain her confidence, he could lure her into some sort of public humiliation.

"I wanted to apologize for… well, for Anton," he said. "For driving him to commit suicide."

For a moment she didn't answer, and he stood there, feeling foolish for attempting so transparent a lie.

"Thank you," she said. "I accept your apology."

He blinked in surprise and took another step toward her. He hadn't expected *that*. He had expected anger, hatred, mistrust — not a quiet acceptance. What had happened to her since their last meeting?

"Are you all right?" he asked. To his own surprise, the concern in his question was sincere.

"I'm fine," she said. "Thank you for your apology, but please go now."

"Why? I mean… what are you doing up here? Why are you sitting like that? Why don't you look at me?"

He could almost hear her smile as she said, "Poor little Stefan! Are you confused? Still caught up in your poses and your intrigues and your feuds? Still obsessed with power? Always afraid someone might be planning to harm you? Well, I'm not planning to harm you, Stefan; I'm not plotting against you, or Serata, or anyone else. Is that why you came? Has my recent absence had you worried?"

"Not about *me*," Stefan said hastily. "We were worried about *you*, Bethany!"

"You needn't be. I'm fine. Go away, Stefan."

"Not until you tell me what you're doing up here."

Bethany sighed, and turned her head to look at him.

"I'm watching the sunrise," she said. "I've been doing it often, of late. Would you care to join me?"

Stefan looked at her, saw her face clearly in the faint fog-reflected glow of approaching dawn; then he turned and fled without another word, almost tumbling down the ladder as he went.

✦

"And did you find little Bethany, then?" Serata asked.

"Yes," Stefan said, uneasily.

"And did you take an appropriately picturesque vengeance on the little meddler?"

Stefan remembered the sight of Bethany's face, the skin blackened and blistered, here and there the flesh burned completely from the bone.

"Vengeance has been done," he said.

He saw no need to say that Bethany had done it herself.

✦

On her rooftop, Bethany watched the sunlight spilling across the sky in billows of color.

Let Stefan and the rest live in the darkness, she told herself, and play their intricate games of power and dominion; she had found something better.

She had found beauty.

She knew that sooner or later the fascination of it might hold her too long, might destroy her; that if she continued her morning vigils she might one day be immolated by the sun's rays.

She didn't mind. If that happened, it happened. She would accept it.

Anton had thought the sun's beauty was worth his life.

Bethany had come to agree with him.

CHAPTER EIGHT
RECONCILIATION

✦

MATT FORBECK

P aul was drinking again, but it wasn't doing him a damned bit of good. He stared at the glass of Glenlivet in his hand and contemplated its golden color, its biting aroma. He brought it to his lips again. It tasted like fire.

He swallowed it carefully, savoring the slow burn. He'd almost sucked half the bottle dry, and it hadn't had the slightest effect. He threw his glass away in anger. It narrowly missed the deejay's head and shattered against the wall behind her, showering the area with sparkling shards of glass and scotch.

The drone of conversation in the Black Hole screeched to a halt. For a long moment, Paul felt the eyes of the last few late-night stragglers upon him. The only sound in the nightclub was the pulsating music pounding out of the speakers near the deejay's booth. Then someone laughed, and the others joined in. Situation normal, all fucked up.

The deejay stared hard at Paul, who met her gaze solidly. Then Paul bared his fangs, and she flinched and looked away. Paul returned to his scotch, and realizing he had thrown away his glass, raised the bottle to his lips.

When he brought it down, Sebastian Melmoth was sliding into the seat across from him in the low booth. Sebastian was smiling broadly at him, but Paul declined to return the gesture. Sebastian's look turned to one of concern.

"My dear chap," Sebastian began, "what is it that's eating at your soul?"

Paul snorted and stayed silent. After a moment, he said, "I can't get drunk."

"Not on alcohol," Sebastian answered, his smile returning. "You're dead. Your heart beats no longer, so the blood cannot carry the booze to your brain. I admit to missing the sensations of a good glass of sherry myself from time to time, but after all, it still tastes the same. It's a small price to pay — don't you think? — for immortality."

Paul grimaced. This man before him — this creature — was the closest thing to a friend he had in this city. Father Steve Singer, his old roommate at Marquette University, was the only person he was closer to. Sebastian had been good to Paul, far kinder than custom demanded, and the very sight of him made Paul sick.

"That's just it, Sebastian. This whole life — no, this... existence. I can sense everything just like I could before, sometimes so sharply it cuts deep. This scotch, I can see it, I can smell it, and I can even taste it, but it has absolutely no effect upon me. It's like this every day. I walk around the city. I see people out there running around, racing against time to do what they can with themselves."

"Yes. Isn't it grand to be free of such constraints? To be able to ignore things like poverty and disease or the ravages of time? To have eternity as the canvas upon which to paint your accomplishments?"

Paul growled. "That's just it. Those 'constraints' are what I considered inspiration. Now I feel like a shadow, unable to affect those around me and, worse yet, to be affected by them."

"But when you feed..." Sebastian began, but when he saw the look of disgust on Paul's face, he stopped. "I see. I forget that you were a man of the cloth before your transformation. Of course these things would be troublesome to someone of your moral standing."

Paul grunted. He was not eager to have Sebastian move too far in this direction. Paul had vowed never to feed on any of God's creatures, and that only left vampires. To drink the blood of another vampire was to be controlled by that creature, unless of course, the creature was dead. Killing a vampire by sucking it dry was the worst crime a vampire could commit, and Paul had done it often. Although he was sure someone as sharp as Sebastian would have suspicions about it, Paul was hardly about to admit to being a diabolist.

"That's part of the problem," Paul said, eager to change the subject. "But what's really bothering me is that I feel so lost."

Sebastian nodded. "Of course. As a priest, your life was defined by your relationship with your God. Now, like the rest of us," Sebastian waved broadly at the few other occupants of the Vampire Club, all of whom were as undead as they, "you are not in God's good graces."

A pained look crossed Paul's face. "How could I be? I've become an abomination, the opposite of what I once was. I feel like staking myself out in the middle of Golden Gate Park and waiting for the sun. At least I'd get to see daylight again one last time."

"Perhaps you're suffering from the bane of vampires everywhere: seasonal affective disorder." Sebastian chuckled at his little joke. "Truly, it can be depressing to always be surrounded by darkness, to never feel the warmth of the sun. But then that should go to show you that we Kindred aren't so different from the kine we once were. If you prick us, do we not bleed?"

Sebastian's demeanor shifted once again to concern. "Many initiates into our little club suffer through their first few months.

You've been unceremoniously served divorce papers by the human race, and like most such splits, it was emotionally messy. But just because you're dead, don't think that you have to give up the things of life. In your particular case, something a wise man once wrote leaps to mind: 'How else but through a broken heart may Lord Christ enter in?' It seems to me that now, more than ever, you're in need of that which got you through your living days."

Paul regarded Sebastian solemnly for a moment before bringing the bottle of scotch to his lips once again. This time when he lowered it, he had another visitor.

It was Tex R. Cainen, the manager of the secretive Vampire Club and its upstairs neighbor, the exclusive Alexandrian Club. Paul could normally hear Tex's boots clanging on the Black Hole's metallic floor from a mile away, but he'd been too caught up in his conversation with Sebastian to pay attention to anything else.

"Howdy, y'all," Tex began in his drawn-out drawl. "Pardon me, Paul, but Sebastian here is needed upstairs. There's some 'administrative duties' he needs to attend to." He flashed a wink at the two of them and turned to go.

"Smashing," said Sebastian. He got up to follow Tex and then turned to make his good-byes to Paul. After one look at the ex-priest's face, Sebastian called after Tex and asked him to return to the table.

As he ushered Tex into the seat he'd just vacated, he said, "My good man, our friend here is struggling with some inner demons, and I thought that perhaps he might benefit from your eloquent perspective on the matter of our mutual condition."

Tex looked up at Sebastian uncertainly. Then he noticed the

bottle in Paul's hand. He flashed Sebastian a knowing smile. "Why, sure thing there, Sebastian. You just head on upstairs quick-like, though. I've got everything well in hand right here."

With a quick smile, Sebastian turned and left. Tex turned to Paul and started in. "Well there, Paul, lemme guess. You just figured out you can't get drunk no more, and unfortunately, that's what you want to do most. Tell me, was this a problem for you when you were breathing? Believe it or not, I think we've got some former AA members around here somewhere. If you like, I can see if I can scare one up for you."

Paul raised a hand to stop Tex's verbal barrage. "No, Tex, thank you. I wasn't an alcoholic before, and apparently there's no longer any chance of me starting down that road."

"What is it, then?" Tex rubbed his lantern jaw with a rough mitt. "A girl?" He raised his eyebrows. "That's it, isn't it? It's always some lady."

"Tex, I'm a priest."

"Well, no you ain't. Not anymore. You're dead, son. The old rules don't apply no more." Tex snapped his fingers. "That's what it is. You know, when you've been cold as long as I have, you tend to forget these things. You're like one of those plant-eaters they got so many of in this city."

"A vegetarian?"

Tex nodded emphatically. "Yep. Your problem, son, is that you're still thinking like a breather. You ain't part of the herd anymore, kid. You're a higher order of being. You shouldn't feel bad about feeding on the herd." His tone became conspiratorial. "That's what this is all about, isn't it?"

Paul was in too much shock to reply. Tex was comparing human beings to cattle, creatures to be slaughtered as the need arose.

"I'll take your silence as a yes. Look here, son, there's nothing to be ashamed of. It kind of turned my stomach at first, too. Hell, most of you tenderfeet actually vomit on your first few times out. Don't worry. You'll get used to it."

Paul picked his jaw up off the table long enough to say, "How?"

Tex shook his head at him knowingly. "Come on, son, didn't you feed on your fellow creatures back when you kept banker's hours? You never had a nice thick steak? Or a barbecued chicken? Almost makes my mouth water just thinking about those things again. It's been a long time since I actually ate any regular *food*. You know what I mean?"

Paul nodded. He didn't know what else to do.

"Look, son, most of us don't feed on the warm ones because we want to. It's because we have to. My point is that you shouldn't feel bad about it. Did you cry over every hamburger you ever chowed on? This isn't a matter of conscience. It's about survival.

"The way I see it, our kind have been around since the beginning. We're not the monsters people think of us as. We're part of the natural order of things, just another step up on the food chain.

"Of course we've got into people's nightmares. Don't the predators always cause fear in the prey? But that shouldn't stop us from being what we are or from doing what we got to in order to survive. Hell, it *can't*."

Tex paused for a moment. "Is any of this sinking in?"

Paul nodded slowly, sadly.

"Well, then, kid, let me give you a little advice." Tex leaned forward across the table. "Make the most of your rookie years. I'm telling you, the hardest thing about being immortal is watching other people grow old and die." He sat back in his seat. "But if you tell anyone I said that, I'll deny it. All right?"

Paul nodded again. He didn't know what to say. He didn't think he knew much of anything right then.

Tex stretched his neck and looked around. The place was empty except for them. "My, it's gotten late so quick. About how far away from here is your place?" Paul started to speak, but Tex pointed a finger to shut him up. "Don't tell me *where* it is, son. I don't want to know. Besides," he pointed at his ear, "the walls, you know."

"What time is it?"

"Fifteen minutes to dawn."

Paul cursed softly. "I'll never make it in time."

Tex grimaced. "Well, I'm sure we can set something up for you. Just wait here, and I'll be right back."

In just a few minutes, Sebastian entered the nightclub, stifling a yawn, and walked up to Paul's booth. "Well, Tex tells me you two were 'shooting the shit' and lost track of time. I suppose I should have mentioned it after we finished talking. After all, it was getting early even then.

"Tex asked me to make his good-byes to you on his behalf, since he's in a bit of a hurry to get home himself. As you know, you're welcome to spend the night here. We have no other guests tonight, so you'd have the aft hold all to yourself."

Paul stood up, leaving the bottle on the table. "I don't really have much of a choice, do I?"

"No," Sebastian smiled crookedly, "not really."

Sebastian led Paul to a door in the back of the club. It opened onto a dark chamber lit only by the dimness filtering in behind Sebastian and Paul. The floor of the hold was covered with futons and pillows. A metal stairway led up into the darkness.

"You'll have to pardon there not being any lights in here, but most of us are used to the darkness by now. Make yourself as comfortable as you can," Sebastian suggested. "Perhaps we'll continue our conversation in the morning."

Paul threw himself down on the cushions and was asleep before the door shut behind him, sealing him into the darkness.

He woke up early the next evening as he always did. He was amazed that he had slept so soundly. If Sebastian or Tex had wanted to, they could have had someone come down and dispose of him during the day. It wasn't that Paul didn't trust them, but they were vampires. Then again, so was he.

Paul got to his feet and stumbled forward, feeling for the door. Eventually he found it, and he stepped back into the Black Hole. He knew that it must be barely twilight outside, even though the portholes in the grounded pleasure yacht that housed the Vampire Club had been painted over too thickly for any light to pass. Paul had always been an early riser, and vampirehood hadn't changed that fact, just the hour at which he rose. Likely Sebastian was still asleep.

Paul walked through the dark, empty nightclub and exited through the front door. He found himself in a room known as the Eternal Pageant. It was lit with red spots, and paintings of the 13 vampire clans were displayed on one wall, while a mural depicting a vampire's path to Golconda, a kind of vampirical heaven, filled the other.

Along the wall with the mural, a stairway led to the upper deck. There were two other doors in the room. One led to the library, and the other to Sebastian's sanctum. Paul strode up to the second door and listened at it. He heard nothing. He tried the door but it was locked.

For a long moment, Paul considered breaking down the door and killing Sebastian while he slept. Paul had sworn to help humanity by destroying the creatures that would feed upon them. The death of the owner of the Vampire Club would be a horrible blow to the creatures of San Francisco. It would put them on notice that they were no longer the predators but the prey.

But Sebastian had been a friend to Paul. And Paul had never seen him kill anybody or, for that matter, do anyone any sort of harm. Who was Paul to judge him? Didn't he have murderous cravings of his own?

Paul was tired of the slaughter. He'd killed several vampires since he'd been fanged, but there were only so many of the creatures he could destroy before drawing attention to himself and getting caught up in a war for his life with every other vampire in San Francisco.

The only other alternative was to leave town, but he had come to enjoy the city. He had made some friends here, including some vampires — like Sebastian — and he was reluctant to simply throw them away. Anyhow, running would do no good. He'd run out of Milwaukee — he understood that now — and if he didn't stop soon, he might never put an end to it. Also, what good was he doing with his life, simply killing a few vampires and then moving on? How was that helping anyone, really? More vampires simply sprang up in their place. It was impossible to stop them.

He was being swallowed up by death, and if something didn't give soon, he was afraid for what he might do — or become.

Cursing himself for a fool, Paul silently turned and left.

Upstairs in the Alexandrian Club, Paul stepped into a phone booth. First he phoned for a cab. Then he dialed up Marty Chin. Chin was another friend — a breather — an information trader who had realized that having Paul in his debt could only work to his favor. It was only with Chin's help that Paul had been able to purchase a place of his own in which to live. Most real-estate agents wouldn't meet with anyone after dark, so Chin had acted as Paul's proxy in the matter. And Chin had done him other favors as well. Paul trusted him as much as anyone else in this city.

"This is Marty Chin. May I help you?" Chin's voice came over the phone, slightly tinted by his Chinese accent.

"Hi, Marty."

"Father!" Chin seemed genuinely glad to hear from him. "What is it I can do for you?"

Paul told him.

When the cab arrived, Paul got in hurriedly and gave the cabby the address that Marty had supplied. He knew he was failing to hide his agitation. The cabby kept one bloodshot eye on him the entire trip, but Paul ignored him.

St. Jude's was in a run-down part of town. According to Chin, it had been scheduled to be closed several years ago due to lack of attendance, but apparently the bishop had never gotten around to actually giving the order.

When he walked in through the front door, Paul was surprised for a moment that he hadn't instantly been struck down. The power of God, he remembered, only worked against a creature like himself if directed by the will of a believer. Since no one had actively opposed his entry, he had been able to stride freely into the church.

The church was old and in poor repair, but it was free of dust and cobwebs. Some of the lights had burned out, and those that were working were dim. Votives burned softly in a niche off to the left. It seemed as if no one else was there.

Keeping his head down, Paul crept slowly down the center aisle like the prodigal son returning home, trying not to make too much noise on the creaking floorboards. After stepping on a particularly loud one, Paul looked up. His eyes darted straight to the crucifix hanging over the altar.

Like Christ, Paul had died and been resurrected, but what good had come to the world? He was a creature of evil. He caught his breath and lowered his head in shame. He made his way into a pew and got down on his knees.

He reached into the breast pocket of his brown bomber jacket and pulled out a large wooden cross. The lower end of it had been sharpened to a point so it could be used as a stake.

It was an instrument of both good and evil. The fact that it could keep other vampires at bay had reinforced his faith in God — that was his salvation. But he also used it to kill those creatures — people not too different from those they once lived among. That was his damnation.

Sebastian had been right. Vampires weren't so different from the living. Some of them fed on animals, just like most people did, often without even killing the creatures. And some of them were horrible, cruel bastards that did their best to scare the hell out of their victims before killing them, getting high on the adrenaline coursing through their hot blood. As a priest, Paul had heard many confessions. He knew that the Kindred weren't the only ones who harbored such darkness in their souls.

Paul was sick with himself. When his life had been torn from him, he'd been enraged. He'd turned that wrath upon those who shared his fate, thinking that by destroying them, he could cleanse the horrible stains on his own soul. But doing evil to evil was still evil.

But he wasn't entirely irredeemable, was he? Was anyone — even a vampire? In his short time in San Francisco, both Sebastian and Tex had shown him friendliness, even kindness. But in this world of darkness, such acts were precious and few.

If Paul thought he was worthy of it, he might try to bring the word of God to the Kindred. He had read Sebastian's "History of the Camarilla" in the Vampire Club's library, and he knew that no one had ever tried such a thing before. Who would be strong enough to be a missionary to the Kindred? If you were a human and knew so much about them, they would most likely kill you. And all vampires, by definition, would have difficulty condemning sinners for the same sins they were committing.

No. Too much had happened. There was too much blood on his hands for him to ever forgive himself.

Paul suddenly realized that he was crying. Crimson tears dripped slowly down his cheeks, contrasting sharply with his pale skin. He wiped his face carefully with his fingers and then cleaned the blood off on his pants.

Then there was a hand on his shoulder. "Are you all right, my son?"

Paul nearly jumped out of his skin. He spun around on his knees and looked up to see an elderly nun gazing down at him. He had been so engrossed with his own thoughts, he hadn't heard her come up behind him. She seemed nearly as startled as he was, but she had barely even flinched. He could see the concern etched on her wrinkled face, although it was mostly in shadows from the light framing her from overhead.

"You seem troubled, my son. Is something wrong?" She gestured at the stains on his shirt where some of his tears had fallen unnoticed. "Have you been hurt?"

Paul stared at the vibrant red marring his white shirt. "Yes, sister," he managed to get out. "I have." He looked up into her eyes and saw only a person's desire to help a stranger. Perhaps there was still hope after all.

"God forgives all my son, as long as you are truly repentant. It seems to me that you are ready for such a blessing."

"Are you sure, sister?"

"I could call for the priest. Would you like to make your reconciliation?"

Paul stood up and took the nun's hand in his own. "Yes, sister, that's exactly what I want." And with that, he stepped out of the pew and strode out of the church, back into the cold November night.

Paul walked down the deserted street until he reached a basketball court. There was a pay phone there under a street light, and he picked up the receiver and dialed a number he knew by heart. It had once been his own.

It was two hours later in Milwaukee, but Father Steve Singer had not yet gone to bed. He was reading by himself when the phone rang. He picked it up, and on the other end of the line, there was a voice he had given up hope of ever hearing again.

"Paul," he said, "is that really you?"

"Yes, Steve, it's me. And I need your help."

Paul told Steve about his night and about the epiphany he'd had in the church. He was going to bring light into the darkness and become God's first messenger to the vampires. "But first I need you to do something for me, Steve."

"Yes? Anything."

Paul took a deep breath before he began.

"Bless me, Father, for I have sinned. My last confession was... a lifetime ago."

CHAPTER NINE
RUINS

✦

JIM MOORE

I.

I think there must be a fine line between love and hatred, because what I feel for Donna Cambridge certainly has a little of both running through it. It was Wednesday night and I stared at the couple walking along the path from the Alexandria Club toward the limousine that waited for them. Donna Cambridge and Vannevar Thomas. They made a stunning couple, and even people who didn't know them paused in conversation or at the very least watched them intently as they walked past. Vannevar was smiling, whispering in Donna's ear. Donna was laughing in response, a musical sound that sent wires of pain through my entire being. At that moment I hated them both for their beauty and for the love they so obviously shared. Even more, I loved her with all my being.

Once, long ago, I had held Donna in my arms, had kissed her skin and made love to her. She'd been engaged to marry me, and we would have lived happily ever after, just like in the fairy tales. I cursed myself for ever losing her, for ever letting her slip away. Mostly, I cursed myself for not realizing what I'd had in Donna until it was too late. I stayed where I was long after the limo had moved on, still thinking about her and wishing I could go into the past and make everything right.

The air was humid and the fog was building again; another night in the city by the bay. I'd come back to San Francisco almost a month earlier, compelled by a desperate need to remember when my life had been worth living. So far the only thing that had gone well was bartering my right to stay in town with the prince of the city, Vannevar Thomas — the man who held all the cards and even held the hand of my Donna. Much as I wanted to, I couldn't bring myself to blame Vannevar for anything that had gone wrong. I couldn't even be mad at him for exiling me from the city in the first place. Everything else in my life was a pale joke and not even a very funny one.

Fifteen years had mellowed my anger substantially, taken the burning hatred for Joe and turned it into a cold, bitter resentment of the cruel thing he'd done to me when he gave me the "gift" of eternal life. Life as a warped reflection from a fun house mirror. I still held a grudge, don't misunderstand me, but I understood his reasons better in hindsight. All his life — human and vampiric alike — Joe had been the outsider, so ugly that most only felt repulsion for him, and so frustrated that even his own family had trouble handling his violent temper. All except for Donna, his sister and my one-time fiancée.

Fifteen years had done nothing to calm down Joe's hatred for me. He hated me even more now than he had back then, a thought that had boggled my mind when we met at Vannevar's offices a month earlier. Thinking back on the occasion, I could feel the anger grow in my chest, swelling beside the fear that was always there. I won't lie about that; whenever I reflect on the tortures Joseph Cambridge put me through when he Embraced me — tortures both physical and mental — I can feel the fear bloom in the back of my throat. The fear always makes me hungry for blood, the only food my system can tolerate and certainly a better taste than the acrid flavor of my remembered tortures.

The fog grew thicker still, and I felt the first fat droplets of rain slide off the battered Stetson on my brow. I was preparing for the hunt, trying to think of a suitable place to find a new victim, when I felt the hand press down on my shoulder. I stared at the massive blue claw for a long second, eyes wide and knees weak, before I hastily stepped away from the shadows.

Joe Cambridge followed only a few seconds later. As was almost always the case, I noticed the sheer size of my enemy first. Joe towered above me, his toady face looming broad and malevolent against the shadowed trees and dark gray sky. Joe stepped forward another pace, and the expression he wore changed from a scowl to a sneer. "Well, well, well. Look what I found."

"Don't touch me, Cambridge. Just get the hell away from me. I don't want any trouble." Despite my best efforts, the fear still trembled deep inside, shaking my voice just enough for both of us to notice. "Vannevar Thomas made his ruling, and you'd do well to abide by it."

Joe just smiled, the false face he wore hiding the fangs he bared with the action, and chuckled deeply in the back of his throat. "I wouldn't dream of hurting you, Jeremy. I don't need to. I always abide by the letter of the law. Besides, just watching you squirm while Donna walks on the arm of Vannevar Thomas is all I need to see to let me know that you're already hurting."

I flared at the barb, stepping forward before I even realized what I was doing. Joseph just smiled, nodding his encouragement. "That's right, pretty boy, why don't you show me what a man you are. Take your best shot." The words were barely above a whisper, loaded with

206

menace. Realizing that I'd stopped myself before it was too late, Joe continued. "Hmm. I rather thought you'd back down. You're not quite that stupid."

Joe moved closer, leaning within inches of my face and grinning evilly. "What if I gave you one free shot? Would you take it? Do you think you could hurt me?"

"I—"

"Hell, Cambridge, I'd take you up on it." The voice was casual, familiar. I felt myself relax slightly. "'Course, Jerry always was kind of a wuss when it came to you." Dawson winked at me and grinned amiably, letting his facial expressions take some of the sting from his words. He was leaning against the tree beside which I had watched my lost love walking with another man only a few minutes earlier, his hands resting against his belt. Dawson never seemed nervous about anything, a quality that I've grown to respect as time has passed. He was dressed the same as always, in a set of clothes that looked like it belonged on an extra from *Urban Cowboy*, right down to the lump of chewing tobacco in his mouth.

"Who the hell are you?" Joseph took the interruption with less grace than I did. His thick lips pulled away from jagged teeth, and his voice sounded much less serene than moments before.

"My name's Dawson," his strong Texas accent and jovial smile lent him an aura of confidence that I've always envied. "I'm an old friend of Jerry's, and I figured I'd track him down so's we could chew the fat for a while." Dawson's eyes ran the length of Joe's frame as he spoke, and his grin grew even wider. "Looks like you had the same idea, Joe. Want to join us?" Dawson winked at me again. "I think it'd be real interesting."

Joe Cambridge smiled broadly, exposing row after row of razor sharp teeth as the Mask dropped away from his face. "No, I'm sure I can find Jeremy and finish our discussion later." The giant started walking away, then turned back to Dawson with another quick smile that didn't quite reach his eyes. "It's nice to know Jeremy's made new friends. Life can be so hard without them."

Dawson flashed a small smirk, paused and spit a wad of brown juice from his mouth. The spit missed Joe's foot by mere inches. "Hell, Joe. Ya'll keep practicin' how to play nice and you might even make a few friends of your own."

Cambridge stared at the glob of spent tobacco juice next to his foot, looked back at the man leaning against the tree, and then he threw his head back and laughed out loud. "You're a funny man, Mr. Dawson. Very funny. Rest assured, I have plenty of friends. You'd be amazed how many friends I have."

"Naw, shit always gathers a mess of flies." Dawson stepped away from the tree and sauntered over to where I stood watching the banter between the two other Kindred like a man watching a tennis match. "Back home, when the shit gets too thick we just scrape it up and toss it in the mulch pile. Nothing better as fertilizer."

"A good night to you, Mr. Dawson." He turned and looked at me as he finished, reweaving the illusion that he was only human in the process. "We'll talk later, Jeremy."

"Hey, listen. I sure didn't mean to break up the party. But I'm real good at keeping secrets if there was something you needed to say to Jerry. Hell, with me here you even have a witness, someone to prove you didn't defy the prince's orders." Dawson's eyes were sparkling, filled with good humor.

Cambridge stepped back into the shadows, his massive form fading from view. "I don't need to break Vannevar's rules. No direct harm will come to your little friend. I've already arranged to make certain of that." There was a great deal of gloating in the sound of Joseph's voice as he continued. "Jean-Claude sends his regards, Jeremy."

Ice filled my veins at his last words. Silence reigned for several moments as Dawson and I listened for sounds around us. Finally Dawson gestured toward the truck in front of the Alexandria Club, and started walking that way, never bothering to see if I was following him. As always, I did.

When we were safely in the truck, Dawson started the engine, cranked the stereo to near full volume and pulled out into the light traffic. I looked out the front window and watched the street move slowly past, picking up speed as we went. "Thanks, Dawson. That's another one I owe you."

"Shit, Jeremy. It ain't like I'm ever gonna collect. Stop trying to keep tabs on favors owed. It just ain't worth the time it takes." He paused for a minute, listening to the radio and thumping the steering wheel to the beat of a country-western song. Then he sighed mightily and placed a friendly hand on my shoulder. "You might want to watch out for Cambridge. Word on the street says he's got a bullet or twenty with your name on 'em."

I snorted at that. "No shit. He's got every Nosferatu in town giving me the cold shoulder. It's a sad world when even the other sewer rats won't talk to you."

"Yeah, you guys ain't normally picky about who you talk with, unless it's business. Old Joe's got more connections in this town than just about anyone 'cept the prince." Dawson rolled his window down part of the way and spit the wad of tobacco out of his mouth. "Damn, that stuff tastes foul after a few hours. Wish I could give that habit up. But it ain't like it's gonna give me cancer or anything, is it?"

"Not in this lifetime. How the hell can you put that crap in your mouth? The very thought of anything but blood and I'm ready to gag."

"That's just 'cause yer a pussy, Jerry," he said with a laugh. "It took about five months of practice. These days I can even eat a five course meal and never flinch, but it still doesn't do anything for me. Great for meeting with the kine in public though." He paused for a few seconds, and then looked at me from the corner of his eye as he eased the truck around another corner. "You can tell me to shut up if you want, Jerr, but I think you need to stop pining away for that little blond girl." There was a long silence while he waited for my answer, but none was coming his way. I knew he was right. I just didn't care. "Comes a time when you have to realize it's over and get on with your life. She's with another man for fifteen years now, and like as not she's Blood Bound to him. She ain't gonna come running back to you."

"Let's not talk about that, okay?"

"Not a problem." Dawson shook his head, failing in his attempt to hide his disgust over the situation. "So, other than Cambridge and his blue cronies wanting to stake you in the sunlight, how's life been treating you?"

I looked at my friend and laughed. The sound was bitter, even to my own ears.

II

I spent the rest of the night just hanging around with Dawson.
We'd been in town for over a month, and whatever Dawson's business
in San Francisco was, he'd been too busy to visit. Counting my
friend's intervention earlier in the evening, this was twice we'd been
together since we first arrived. I had too much time on my hands,
Dawson had too little.

The first shades of false dawn were making themselves known
when I finally made it back to my family home on Nob Hill. The
lights were still burning in the living room windows, and I sighed,
fully expecting another confrontation with my mother. At least once
a week she felt obligated to explain how much she worried about me,
and every time she did, the night ended with her in tears. I love my
mother; she is a kind, giving woman, and she took me back in after
fifteen years of not seeing me — she even accepted me after finding
out about what I am. But, damn, that woman can really get on my
nerves when she starts harping about my lifestyle, or rather, the lack
thereof.

I slid my key into the lock and opened the door, closing and
locking the front entrance behind me. Despite the brilliant light from
the living room, there was no sign of my mother anywhere. Nor was
Alicia awake, but that didn't surprise me. I set about turning off all
the lights and was wending my way toward the basement and my
haven. I felt the first pull of exhaustion seeping into me as the sun
started to rise. There was no danger yet, as the brilliance from outside
would not actually enter the house for a while yet, but I could still
feel the demands of my body as it called for the deathlike trance that

passed for sleep these days. I could resist the call if I wanted to, but the cost was always high: a feverish twitching in my body and soul that demanded payment in full for my insolence. Sort of like a hangover without the benefit of getting good and drunk in advance. At least with Daylight Saving Time in effect I had longer spans of time to enjoy consciousness.

Just as I was opening the door leading to the basement, the phone gave out a shrill cry, the sound loud enough in the silence to startle me. Without even thinking about it, I grabbed for the phone in the hallway and answered, my primary concern being the sound sleep of everyone else in the house. "Hello?"

"Jeremy?" The voice on the phone sent chills through me automatically. Joe Cambridge. Joe should not have had my unlisted number, but he did. "I just wanted to express my condolences, I know that your father's death was hard on you, but to have your mother so grievously injured... Well, I am truly sorry." The voice made a lie of his words, but I didn't even ponder the facts as I reacted.

"What are you talking about, Cambridge? What have you done?"

"Why, nothing at all, Jeremy. You offend me. I was talking to you when the accident occurred. Besides, I don't even drive."

"What are you talking about?"

"You mean you don't know?" The gloating voice was maddening. "Your dear mother has had a very bad accident. I'm afraid she's in critical condition." Silence then for several eternal seconds. "Well. I'm sorry to be the bearer of bad news, and I wish I could tell you more, but I only just heard about it myself. Besides, the sun is coming up. Sweet dreams, Jeremy."

The dial tone hummed in my ear a few seconds later, and finally I moved, crawling into my basement and hiding in a small supply closet as the sun finally reached the windows of the house. I was cold and numb, and sleep came upon me slowly, pulling me deep into its freezing embrace.

III

I awoke to the fading screams from my nightmares, feeling the dream recede even as I shook the sleep from my body. The room was cold, not that it mattered; everything around me was as cold and lifeless as I felt. After a few seconds, the thoughts finally came back, blowing the remaining fragments of my nightmares into so much dust. I remembered Joe's smirking voice on the phone and what had prompted the call in the first place. My stomach tried doing a few back flips as the memory grew. Pulling myself from my cubbyhole in the storage closet, I adjusted my clothes and climbed up the stairs, preparing for whatever might wait beyond the cellar door.

There was nothing, only silence and more darkness. It only took a few minutes to click on the lights in the living room and ascertain that no one but me was in the house. I felt a cold lump of dread ice over my insides. No one was home, and I'd looked and found no message on the premises. I finally checked the garage on the side of the house and discovered that there was no car parked behind the closed door, only more darkness.

I checked the answering machine: Three messages asking that my mother, Anita, call this friend or that one, nothing else. No message from my mother or from Alicia. I started calling hospitals.

After over an hour of playing phone-tag between different receptionists at several locations, I found out that my mother was in the Intensive Care Unit at San Francisco General. Visiting hours ended at 9 P.M. sharp, but I could still see her for a few minutes if I hurried. I called a cab; sometimes the extra expense is necessary.

Throughout the journey, I replayed the events of the previous night again and again. One sentence from Joseph Cambridge kept creeping back into my mind: "Jean-Claude sends his regards." I had literally purchased the right to stay in town at Jean-Claude's expense: I'd bought immunity for all past crimes by delivering the Settite's heart, along with the heart of Darrius Stone, to Vannevar Thomas, the prince of San Francisco. With the heart in his possession, Thomas could literally destroy Jean-Claude at any time with little more than a gesture.

In all honesty, I would have been a little upset if I'd been the bargaining tool in such a situation. Small wonder that the leader of the Children of Set would take offense. I had no idea where I could find the leader of the Settites, but I suspected the Sand Snake would find me when he was ready.

I thought about the exact words that Vannevar Thomas had used in regards to Joe Cambridge leaving me alone. The man had said that no direct action on Joe's part against me would be tolerated. Simply letting Jean-Claude know who had bartered his heart into the prince's hands could not be called a direct action. But the end result would be the same either way...

I was pulled out of my reverie by the voice of the cab driver. "Hey, mister. We're here." The man promptly lifted the flag and turned to smile at me with a deep concern on his face. "I hope everything's okay, mister." The thick Middle-Eastern accent made the words sound almost musical. "Me? I hate hospitals. Nothing but pain and suffering in these places. The total's $15.08, please." I handed the driver a twenty and slipped from the back seat before he could start counting change. He called out his thanks and pulled away from the curb. I noticed the cab-driver's name on his license, not that it much mattered to me. The name Amir Shubandabbi meant nothing to me. As I found out later, it meant a great deal to others. Amir was one of Jean-Claude's most faithful informants.

The interior of the hospital was busy, surprisingly so until I realized that it was Thanksgiving night. Plenty of people coming in later than usual and staying later as well to share the holiday with a friend or family member who had ended up in the cold, sterile environment. With my ability to make others ignore me, I had almost no trouble slipping past everyone in the hallways. The only exception was a dark-haired boy sitting with his mother. I heard the whispered words of the child: "Mommy, that man's got blue skin..."

I turned around just in time to see the woman grab her son's hand and squeeze gently. The boy stared at me with one bloodshot eye and then looked to his mother as she spoke absently to him. "What have I told you about lying, Christopher? He looks just as normal as you or me." The woman turned and smiled apologetically at me, only to look back at her son as he spoke again.

"But Mommy..."

"But nothing. You hush now, you might hurt the nice man's feelings." She looked at me again and looked back to her child. "You apologize, right now."

5.

"But—"

"Now, young man, or I'll tell your father about this nonsense." Her voice grew stern.

"I'm sorry, mister."

I smiled back, grateful for the illusions that hid my true appearance from the living. Just the same, the child recoiled from the sight of my bared teeth. "No harm done, Christopher. You be a good boy for your mother."

Christopher, on the verge of crying, nodded quickly. His eyes were threatening tears, and I suspected the infection in his left eye was bad enough without the waterworks. I turned away before I caused the boy any more trouble. I was upset that the child apparently saw past my Mask, but not very upset. No one would believe him, not even his own mother, and I had more pressing matters to attend. Like as not, in later years the ability to see past illusions would fade. I'd run across other toddlers who could still see with more than five senses, but had yet to encounter an adult who could.

When I reached my mother's room I only stayed for a few moments. She was broken and battered, and the tubes running down her throat, forcing air into her lungs, were more than I could stand. The woman I had been raised by was always healthy, always cheerful and vital. What lay in the hospital bed in front of me looked hollow and pale by comparison. She was deathly pale and her veins showed through her skin as if it were nothing more than tissue paper. The bed beside hers held Alicia, the family maid for as long as I could remember. She was asleep, but apparently in better shape than my mother. Both had broken bones and carefully bandaged wounds. The scent of blood was even stronger than the overwhelming stench of the disinfectant, and I was reminded that the time to feed was fast approaching. I walked to my mother's side and leaned over to kiss her forehead gently, but the need for sustenance was almost overwhelming and I stepped back, barely under control.

I grabbed a pen from the clipboard and scribbled a quick note to Alice and my mother. The note said: 'I had to leave. Will be back as soon as I can. All of my love, Jeremy.'

I almost ran from the hospital, cursing myself for my weakness and cursing Joe Cambridge for what he'd made me. Sometimes I almost forgot what I'd become, and when the memory came rushing back, it was twice as bad. When I finally found a place where I felt safe hunting, I located a target and assaulted the man brutally. He was a handsome man, in his mid-thirties, with clothes that spoke of money. I needed the release of tension almost as much as I needed the blood. I stopped myself in time and left the man alive, though just barely. I licked the wounds shut and ran from the area, teeth clenched together and hands balling into fists.

I was moving so fast that I didn't notice Mark Anderson until I literally ran into him. I grabbed his arms and held him up, starting to apologize automatically for almost knocking him down. Then I heard his voice, and the memories soared back. "Jeremy Wyzchovsky? Wix? Damn, I haven't seen you since high school!"

Mark looked me up and down and I returned the favor, trying to reconcile the differences twenty years had made in the captain of the football team. Where there had been nothing but solid muscle years

before, Mark now carried a spare thirty pounds of flab, and he carried each pound poorly. I almost didn't recognize him until he smiled. The expression took years away from him and brought back a hint of the man I'd known so long ago. For a few years we'd been inseparable, then he went to school in New York and I'd never heard from him again. "Shit, Jeremy, you look great!"

"Jesus Christ. Mark? How the hell are you?" There was no awkwardness as we reached out and gave each other ferocious bear-hugs. The years faded away for a second, and we were good friends again, just like old times. Human contact can be a glorious thing; just the simple act of touching another person with affection. You never miss it until you realize that you haven't held a person in friendship or love for a long time. Maybe that's why so many vampires are bitter, and why so many of us refer to ourselves as the Damned. Loneliness must surely be an important aspect of hell. "God, it's great to see you, guy."

"Jeremy. You're crushing me." I hastily stepped back, releasing him from the unintentional death-grip I'd had on his ribs. I tend to forget the benefits of my condition as well, like the ability to crush a man to death without even breaking a sweat. He stepped back also, a smile still on his face and mild shock in his eyes. "Still as strong as you ever were, my man. Where do you work out?" His laughter was music to my ears, and my mind flashed on a hundred other times I'd heard the same sort of laughter from him. In fifteen years I'd almost never thought about Mark Anderson. I was surprised by the intensity of my feelings for him.

We talked for a few minutes, trying to catch up on twenty years in that time. He told me lies about how well he was doing, how much he loved his wife and how much she loved him, and how much he loved his job as the assistant manager at his bank; and I returned the favor by telling him that I was thrilled by my work as a stockbroker. They were good lies, the kind that cause no one pain and make everyone feel better about the failures they've had in life. I think Mark was almost as lonely and depressed as I was.

Finally, Mark looked at his watch and sighed. "Listen, Jeremy, I've gotta get out of here. I've got to meet my wife and her folks for a dinner date in half an hour. But why don't you give me a call later tonight and we can get together tomorrow?" He passed me a card with his business number and his home number, and I promised I'd do just that. I walked away from the meeting with a spring in my step and a stupid smile plastered to my face. I didn't think about Donna or my mother at all. I was happy for the first time in a long, long while.

I left myself open for a world and a half of hurt.

I'd fed, and I was ready to see my mother again despite the knowledge that visiting hours were long since past. I really meant to see her, but I just couldn't bring myself to face the grievous injuries she'd experienced, or the almost-certain knowledge that the wounds were caused by my very presence and my past actions.

Yeah, I know I'm scum, but at least I'm honest about it.

I spent the rest of the night wandering the streets and spiraling back into a self-pitying fugue. Thanksgiving night, and the only company I could manage to find was myself. The only time I paused in my solitary wanderings was when I called Mark and arranged to see him the next night. He wanted to meet for lunch, but I managed to convince him that later was better. With my particular condition, sunlight tends to leave nasty burns — if you manage to survive.

Around 5:30, I finally headed toward the house on Nob Hill where I'd spent as little time as possible while growing up. I guess some things never change, because I still hated being around the place when it was occupied.

I got there after the fire engines had left. The heat was still intense and the blackened, skeletal remains of my family home smoldered and steamed in the pre-dawn morning. I probably would have noticed the burnt-out shell earlier if I'd bothered to look past the shadows chasing my feet, or even remembered to breathe and sniff around for trouble. I stopped dead in my tracks less than a hundred yards from where the front door used to be.

Several people from the neighborhood stared at the carnage, mumbling to themselves and shaking their heads sadly. They were glad it wasn't one of their homes, and some were even saddened that it was the Wyzchovsky place that burned, but most were just there to look on the ruins of another person's world. What had been my mother's world, and mine too, I suppose. What little was left of my human life had been in that building: the trophies I'd won in tennis matches, the photographs from simpler times when the world still had color for me. Gone, lost to a fire that I knew in my heart had been set. I had no proof, nor did I need it. Joseph Cambridge was keeping his word — he was doing me no direct harm. He just made me suffer for ever having met his sister, and made me loathe the fact that he was alive at all. I don't think I've ever hated anyone as much as I hated him right then.

There were two other vampires there, both Nosferatu. They were deep in the shadows, but not really trying to hide from me. I'd seen them in passing, been snubbed by them during my first week in town. The one on the right, dressed in filthy rags and carrying a heavy bag on her shoulder, I recognized as Vika. The other one I could put no name to. Who knows, maybe they were planted by Cambridge, maybe they even started the fire, or maybe they just came to see the action and gather news for the highest bidder — that is what the Nosferatu do best, barter information.

If they'd noticed me, they were very careful not to let me know it. They were talking in subdued whispers, and I decided to listen to what they had to say. There are very few advantages to being a Nosferatu, but one of them comes in the form of acute hearing. My ears are huge, pointy things these days, and I guess that helps. The Mask is a mind trick, and one I'm good at, but it has other applications as well. There was no real effort involved, I just arranged my thoughts and moved carefully through the darkness. They never heard me or saw me as I moved closer to them. I caught a part of their conversation: Vika was talking. "I don't know where they're coming from, but I've seen them everywhere. Every time I turn around, there's another human running around with a bloodshot eye. And it's only one eye, never both of them. Let me tell you something else, Scabby, they can see us for what we are."

"I don't think they're human at all. I was over in China Town last night, doin' a little of the old song and dance for the Dowager, and she tells me they came from under the city. From the ruins beneath us in old San Fran."

"Yeah, I've heard the same. Whoever breaks this baby can write their own check with his lordship, Vannevar. I aim to be the one. Put the word out — I want to know what's what with the bloodshot humans. And tell Cambridge his little prize never showed up at the hospital a second time." The one she addressed as Scabby nodded vigorously and scuttled out of the shadows, hiding behind his own Mask as he went.

I waited for Vika to move, but she stayed where she was, her eyes closed for a few seconds. Then she looked straight at me and smiled. "Hello, Wix." I was a bit shocked, but only a little bit. There are enough vampires out there who can see past the illusions I create that I seldom grow unsettled when they manage to see me. "You're good. I didn't even notice you until a few seconds ago." She turned away from me, heading toward the lawn of the house next door. I was preparing to follow her when she looked over her shoulder and stared at me intently for a few seconds. She pointed to where the conversation had taken place between her and Scabby, and then she spoke. "I know what you must be thinking, what with the accident your mother had and all. But it wasn't me, and it wasn't any of the other sewer rats. We just came to see what was going down." She waited long enough to see me nod, and then she vanished into the darkness.

Where she had been pointing, a small sheaf of papers lay folded into quarters and half buried in the soil; she'd been standing on top of them, and she hadn't moved until Scabby had left the area. I took the papers and unfolded them. The writing was immediately recognizable to me. It was mine. I stared at a photocopy of the pages I'd given to my mother the night I came back into town. The letter was a long, abbreviated history of the events that led to my Embrace, my exile from the city, and the life I'd been living for fifteen years. It told of the Camarilla, the Kindred, the world of vampires. And it mentioned Vannevar Thomas, Donna Cambridge and Joseph Cambridge by name. I grew numb while I stared at the lines of writing — if anyone else had seen these pages, I was in deeper trouble than I wanted to think about.

There was a note scrawled on the back of the pages that was almost equally familiar. It was written in the tight, close letters I recognized as coming from Dawson's pen. *I took this off a corpse on the way to the morgue. Three other copies have been found and reported to the prince by Emily Grange. She's the night shift M.E. and a Ventrue. Rumor has it that Cambridge has been calling for a Blood Hunt. Watch your ass, Jeremy.* There was no signature, but if I'd been in the same position I wouldn't have implicated myself either.

Someone had taken the papers I'd written away from my mother and had been making copies. Cambridge, maybe, but I doubted it. More likely it was one of the Settites, maybe even Jean-Claude himself. Either way I was fucked. Thomas knew about the papers, and I knew for certain he'd be unhappy about them. Cambridge was probably in seventh heaven by now, ready to strike me down the second that Vannevar Thomas agreed to the hunt. I had to give him credit where it was due; the last time he'd completely shattered my life it took him a month. This time he'd managed the feat in less than two days.

The sun was on the rise by the time I left the remains of my family home. For the first time in over ten years I slept in the sewers.

IV

As soon as the sun set, I was on my way. I slipped out of a manhole near the Tenderloin and called Mark Anderson. A man picked up after the third ring, but his voice was unfamiliar. My skin crawled for no reason I could think of when I heard the official sounding voice. "Anderson residence, who may I say is calling?"

"Jeremy Wyzchovsky. I'm calling for Mark Anderson."

"I'm sorry, sir. Could you spell that last name for me?"

"Just tell him it's Wix, he'll know who you mean."

"Please, if you could just spell the last name for me."

"Who am I speaking with?" He paused, and I repeated the question.

"This is Lieutenant John Coleson, San Francisco Police. What is the nature of your call, Mr. Wizlowski?"

I opted not to correct him on the mispronunciation of my last name. "I'm supposed to meet Mark later on tonight. Is everything okay over there?"

"Are you a friend of the family, Mr. Wizlowski?"

"Uh, yeah. Well, I know Mark, we ran across each other last night, and we were going to meet for dinner..."

"I'm sorry to be the one to tell you sir, but I'm afraid Mark Anderson won't be able to meet with you." Oh, I wanted to ask him why, I really did, but I was afraid I already knew the answer to the question. He proved me right when he continued after a few seconds of silence. "I'm afraid Mr. Anderson is dead." He kept right on talking, at least until I'd slammed the phone back into its cradle. I even wiped the phone clean before I left. Not that what passes for my skin these days has any recognizable fingerprints, mind you. I guess I just watch too much television for my own good.

It didn't take too much math to figure out what the hell was going on. Dawson's note said four bodies had been found with my letter to my mother. Mark told me last night that he was going for dinner with his wife and his in-laws. I'd have bet money that all four bodies came from one location, the same one I'd just called on the phone. I'd like to say that I mourned for Mark and his family, but in truth I was just too damned scared to care about them. Everywhere I turned, there was something going wrong. Every person I knew in town seemed destined for pain, simply because they knew me. I'd gotten sloppy after a month with no conflicts, and I never realized just how much trouble I was in when I crossed paths with Joe Cambridge. God damn him for being right. He didn't even have to lift a finger and already my life was falling to pieces.

I hid myself in the shadows until I found another pay phone a few blocks away. Then I called San Francisco General and asked to speak with Alicia White. I spent five minutes waiting on the line, listening to premature Christmas music, before I got a connection to her room. "Hello?"

"Alicia? Hi, it's Jeremy."

"Jeremy? Where are you? You've had your mother worried sick." Her voice was strong, and that was good, but the words she'd just said were even better.

"Mom's awake?"

"Well of course she is. She's in the next bed. Do you want to talk to her?"

"Yeah, please."

There was a few seconds of fumbling, and then my mother's voice came on the phone. "Jeremy? Are you all right? The police told me about the fire. They didn't find anyone in the ruins, but I was worried half to death about you."

"Yeah, Mom. I'm fine. How are you? You didn't look so hot last time I saw you."

"Well, I'm fine, Jeremy. Alicia's doing even better than me. She'll be out of the hospital in the morning, and if my recovery continues like it is right now, I'll be out before Monday."

And there they went again, a dozen little alarm bells ringing in my head, screaming that they didn't let people out of the hospital less than a week after they'd been forced to shove a hose or two down the patient's throat. I forced false levity into my voice. "Heck, sounds like you're doing worlds better. I thought for sure you'd be there at least a couple of weeks with the injuries you sustained."

"Seems everyone here thought that. But I guess there must have been some sort of confusion when they took my x-rays, because they thought there were a lot of broken bones in this old body, but when they checked again, everything was fine except a broken ankle." In her usual way, she deflected any further questions about herself and redirected the conversation back to me. "Are you sure you're okay, Jeremy? Where are you staying? Is there anything I can get you?"

"I'm fine, honest." But I wasn't fine, not at all. I'd seen the way she looked, I'd smelled the blood from what had to be internal bleeding in her body, and here she was sounding like the most damage she'd suffered was to her pride. Either my mother was more robust than I'd ever realized, or something was very, very wrong.

There are humans that serve the Kindred, called ghouls by most of us because they feed on the dead in their own way. They feed on the blood of vampires, and it keeps them young and in fine shape. It can even heal their wounds, the same way that vampires can force their wounds to heal if they have sufficient blood in their systems. What better place than a hospital to slip vampiric blood into the body of a wounded person and speed the healing process? Simple fact #703: If you can get another vampire, or a human, and convince them to drink from your blood three times, you can literally force them to like you, to want to please you and to serve you. It's called the Blood Bond, and I know it works, because that's how vampires ensure the loyalty of their ghouls. My mother had been in the hospital for three nights, and during that time, someone had been feeding her blood. Vampiric blood. I had no solid proof, but again, I didn't need it. Like I said, I saw her on her second night in the hospital, and she looked like death warmed over then. Now, only one night later, she was sounding healthy and cheerful.

I spoke without really paying attention for a few more minutes, and then I said my good nights. I'd called the hospital in the hopes that my mother was recovering, maybe coming out of her coma. Right then I wished that she had never pulled out. Someone had bound my mother to himself through the blood of a vampire, and I was a vampire without many friends in the Kindred community. The thought of seeing my mother again was one I'd have to repress, because I had no way of knowing who she now served, and no way to find out. Vannevar Thomas or Donna Cambridge? Not likely, they had little or nothing to gain except for money, and they had that in spades. Joseph Cambridge or Jean-Claude? One of the two vampires who almost certainly wanted me dead? Distinctly possible. I knew it wasn't Dawson; he'd have no idea where to look, and no reason for doing the deed.

I called information and got the number I needed from the operator. I slipped my quarter into the slot and punched the buttons carefully, as it was the last of my spare change. After seven rings I got an answer. When the person on the line announced where he worked, I asked to speak to his supervisor, Doctor Emily Grange. Less than a minute later, I heard her cool, cultured voice pick up the receiver. "This is Doctor Grange, how can I help you?"

"Doctor, my name is Jeremy Wix. I think we need to talk."

The night went downhill from there. The woman was sharp and definitely knew her business when it came to forensics. She carefully explained to me that the bodies had all been killed in violation of the Masquerade, the most important law of the Camarilla. She detailed the unique patterns of teeth used on the necks of the four people killed and pointed out that all four had been left with a decent amount of blood in their bodies, but not enough to hide that they'd been drained. She went on to discuss the importance of licking wounds, and how breaking the necks of the victims didn't necessarily kill them, but that I'd been fortunate this time. She let me know that Vannevar Thomas had agreed with Joseph Cambridge when my Sire suggested a Blood Hunt. She then heartily recommended that I turn myself in before it was too late, because apparently half the Kindred in the city were perfectly willing to make me their personal mission, especially in light of the substantial reward for my capture. A reward offered by none other than Joe Cambridge.

I hung up the phone when she started in on my lack of forethought for the third time. I remembered Vika's comments to Scabby earlier, the talk about how the strange people with the bloodshot eyes had come from the ruins beneath the city. Ruins largely unexplored, and certainly safer than any haven I might find in the surface world.

It took the rest of the night to find an entrance, but I did find one. I can't leave San Francisco, tempting as the idea is. There's too much unresolved, too much that isn't settled between me and my Sire, me and Vannevar Thomas. There was the situation between myself and the Settites in town, especially Jean-Claude and Darrius Stone. And then there's Donna Cambridge.

I love her, with all of my heart I love Donna Cambridge. And I guess a part of me hates her, too. I keep thinking that with just a gesture or two and a few words, she could probably clean this entire mess up. She could let the prince know that I've never been that stupid, that I'd never leave so obvious a trail. She could make him understand that her brother hates me more than anything he's ever seen. She could even resolve my worst problem, the Settites, just by convincing Vannevar Thomas that they are the likeliest choice for everything that's gone down in the last few days.

I keep seeing Donna laughing with Vannevar Thomas, the

sophisticated, handsome man who rules over the Kindred in San
Francisco. I see her laughing and smiling, holding his hand when
once upon a time she held mine. I thought that maybe she'd found it
in her heart to forgive me, but now I know better.

I think about the ruins my life have become, and I think about
the differences between love and hate. I see Donna laughing at
Thomas' little whispered joke. I hope the leftovers that rest beneath
the city are empty and dark, with nothing moving, nothing to disturb
me. Maybe if it's dark enough, I won't see her anymore, I won't think
of what it was like before my life was destroyed by her brother the first
time, and I won't keep hearing her laughter echoing in my mind.
When she's gone from there, from the bitter memories in my heart
and soul, perhaps I'll know peace again. I'll know only the darkness.

✦

EPILOGUE

MONSTERS, MONSTERS, EVERYWHERE...

✦

T hey crowd our imagination. They hide under our beds. They lurk within the dark recesses of our primal unconsciousness. You can't run and you can't hide; it's going to get you. The beast, the ravager, the *Lusus Naturæ*. What is it, and why do we fear it?

What is its name?

Always we have had our Fiends. They have long fired the romantic imagination of both priest and poet alike. At one time, we called them Trolls, they were later named Demons, and then they were Witches who brewed evil potions. Still later, the Monster was said to be the hungry Wolf, the Bogeyman and the Godzilla of Cold War terror. Finally, some called it human ignorance and intolerance. For a time, they tried to tell us that Monsters didn't exist at all, that everything about the universe was either known or would soon be known.

But now we know better. We have made our reacquaintance with the Beast. We have learned its true name.

Now we understand the expanse of eternity, its unimaginable infinitude, the chaos of its structure, and we understand our own petty insignificance. Now we have admitted the magnitude of the problems we face and of our seeming inability to affect change on the scale necessary to save ourselves.

Today, we have caught a glimpse of reality and have seen truth behind the veil. We have come full circle and rediscovered the Fiend. We have regained our ancient heritage. We have found that to which we have given so many names — the source of our mortal terror.

We have found the enemy... and it is us.

We humans are searchers, forever looking for the uncomfortable truths of our human condition. Searching within ourselves for that which is unclean, uncertain, impure — for that which has no name. By looking at the monsters we create, we gain new insight into our "darker half." These fiends express what we are at the deepest and most inaccessible levels of our unconsciousness. Since time immemorial, they have given us a connection to our animal self — the fulfillment of an unadulterated, emotional vitality and the promise of brutal justice.

The vampire is the quintessential fiend, for the vampire is so much our own reflection. Vampires feed as we feed, by killing, and through death can feel the same dread, guilt and longing for escape. They are trapped in the same cycle of fast, feast and purge. They, like us, seek redemption, purity and peace. The vampire is the poetic expression of our deepest fears and the shadow of our most primal urges.

Just as the hero of legend must descend into the pit of Purgatory to face his tormentor, to overcome personal weaknesses, and finally to be cleansed to return home with the gift of fire, so must we descend into the depths of our own souls and return to life with the secrets we have won. That is the real journey of Prometheus. It is the meaning of the myth. Only by embarking on such a journey can we discover our true selves and look into the mirror.

The allure of this promise of spiritual connectivity is nigh to irresistible. But, in the end, it is a most disturbing undertaking. You must take heed and step carefully — for no journey is ever without its perils. Do not look into your own soul unless you are willing to confront what you find there.

So remember:

There are no such thing as Monsters...

IT ALL BEGAN WITH VAMPIRE: THE MASQUERADE®,
THE STORYTELLING GAME OF PERSONAL HORROR.

VAMPIRE: THE MASQUERADE® IS A UNIQUE INTERACTIVE EXPERIENCE THAT LETS YOU LIVE THE UNLIFE OF THE KINDRED. YOU PLAY THE PART OF A VAMPIRE IN A STORY THAT UNFOLDS AROUND YOU, AND YOUR DECISIONS CONTROL THE OUTCOME OF THE ADVENTURE.

IN VAMPIRE: THE MASQUERADE®, YOU HAVE POWER UNDREAMPT OF BY MORTALS.

YOU MAKE YOUR OWN RULES.

YOU CHOOSE YOUR OWN MORALITY.

YOU ARE IN COMPLETE CONTROL.

BUT BEWARE, BEFORE YOU GAZE INTO THE ENDLESS NIGHT, YOU MUST BE PREPARED TO FACE THE DARKNESS THAT LIES WITHIN YOURSELF.

In the dark hours of the night the shadows come to life...

White Wolf Publishing presents a premiere line of fiction based on the tragic, sexy, dark, and gothic world of VAMPIRE: THE MASQUERADE®.

VAMPIRE:THE MASQUERADE® fiction explores all the hidden aspects of the world of Vampires as only White Wolf can. It is a no-holds-barred descent straight into the depths of personal hell as the mysteries of the kindred are unearthed between the pages...

LIVE AS ONLY THE UNDEAD CAN, AND DARE TO KNOW THEIR SECRETS.

LOOK FOR THE LOGO!

Available at your favorite bookseller, or mail in the coupon for convenient ordering

Yes! Please send me the following:

☐ Vampire: The Masquerade®   1-56504-029-5   WW2002 $28.00US/$38.35CAN

☐ Beast Within   1-56504-086-4   WW11001 $4.99US/$6.99 CAN

☐ Bloodwar: Vol.1   1-56504-840-7   WW12400 $5.99US/$7.99 CAN

☐ Unholy Allies: Vol. 2   1-56504-841-5   WW12401 $5.99US/$7.99 CAN

☐ The Unbeholden: Vol. 3   1-56504-842-3   WW12402 $5.99US/$7.99 CAN

☐ As One Dead   1-56504-875-X   WW11517 $5.99US/$7.99 CAN

For Visa/Mastercard and Discover card orders, call 1-800-454-WOLF

White Wolf Publishing
Attn: Ordering Department
780 Park North Boulevard
Suite 100
Atlanta, Georgia 30021

Please add $1.50 for shipping and handling for the first book and .40 for each book thereafter. No cash, stamps or C.O.D.s. All orders shipped within 6 weeks via postal service book rate. Canadian orders require $2.00 extra postage, paid in U.S. dollars through a U.S. banking facility.

Name_____

Address_____

_____

City _____

State _____ Zip Code _____

I have enclosed $_____in payment for the checked book(s). Payment must accompany all orders. ® Please send a free catalog